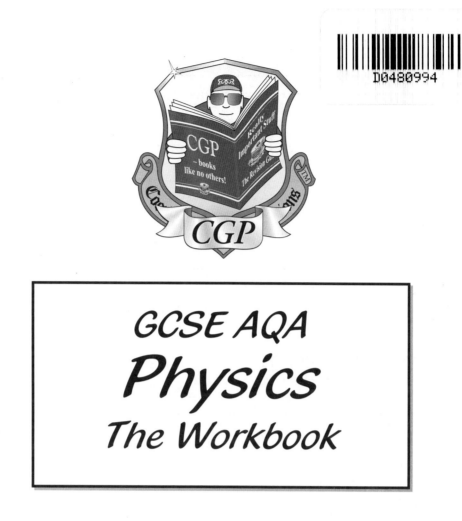

GCSE AQA
Physics
The Workbook

This book is for anyone doing **GCSE AQA Physics**.

It's full of **tricky questions**... each one designed to make you **sweat**
— because that's the only way you'll get any **better**.

There are questions to see **what facts** you know. There are questions
to see how well you can **apply those facts**. And there are questions
to see what you know about **how science works**.

It's also got some daft bits in to try and make the whole
experience at least vaguely entertaining for you.

What CGP is all about

Our sole aim here at CGP is to produce the highest
quality books — carefully written, immaculately presented
and dangerously close to being funny.

Then we work our socks off to get them
out to you — at the cheapest possible prices.

Contents

Published by CGP

Editors:
Helena Hayes, Felicity Inkpen, Julie Wakeling, Sarah Williams.

Contributors:
Steve Coggins, Paddy Gannon, Dr Giles R Greenway, Frederick Langridge,
Barbara Mascetti, John Myers.

ISBN: 978 1 84762 678 3

With thanks to Michael Birch, Mark A Edwards, David Ryan, Karen Wells and Dawn Wright
for the proofreading.

Pages 34, 98 and 99 contain public sector information published by the Health and Safety
Executive and licensed under the Open Government Licence v1.0.

Groovy website: www.cgpbooks.co.uk

Printed by Elanders Ltd, Newcastle upon Tyne.
Jolly bits of clipart from CorelDRAW®

Based on the classic CGP style created by Richard Parsons.

Heat Radiation

Q1 a) Tick the correct boxes to show whether each of the following statements is true or false.

True False

i) Heat energy can be transferred by radiation, conduction and convection. ☐ ☐

ii) Conduction involves the transfer of energy between moving particles. ☐ ☐

iii) Hot objects do not absorb infrared radiation. ☐ ☐

iv) Convection always involves a moving liquid or gas. ☐ ☐

v) Cold objects do not emit infrared radiation. ☐ ☐

b) Write out corrected versions of the **false** statements.

....

....

Q2 Complete the following sentences by circling the correct words.

a) Dark, matt surfaces are **good** / **poor** absorbers and **good** / **poor** emitters of infrared radiation.

b) The best surfaces for radiating infrared are **good** / **poor** absorbers and **good** / **poor** emitters.

c) Silvered surfaces are **good** / **poor** absorbers and **good** / **poor** emitters of infrared radiation.

d) The best surfaces for solar hot water panels are **good** / **poor** absorbers and **good** / **poor** emitters.

Q3 Each sentence below contains two mistakes. Write out a correct version of each.

a) Infrared radiation is emitted from the centre of hot solid objects, but not from liquids or gases.

....

....

b) Only some objects absorb infrared radiation — the bigger the difference in temperature between an object and its surroundings, the slower the rate of heat transfer.

....

....

Q4 Give a scientific reason why steel **electric kettles** are often made very **shiny**.

....

....

Heat Radiation

Q5 Tick the correct boxes below to show whether the sentences are true or false.

True   False

a) The amount of infrared radiation absorbed by a surface depends only on its colour. ☐ ☐

b) The hotter a surface is, the more infrared radiation it radiates. ☐ ☐

c) Good absorbers of infrared radiation are also good emitters of infrared radiation. ☐ ☐

d) White glossy surfaces absorb infrared radiation better than dark matt surfaces. ☐ ☐

e) Some solar panels are designed to absorb radiation from the Sun to heat water for washing or heating a building. ☐ ☐

Q6 Three flasks, each containing 100 ml of water, are placed in closed boxes. The water in the flasks and the air in the boxes are at different temperatures, as shown.

A — Air in box 55°C — Water 60°C

B — Air in box 50°C — Water 65°C

C — Air in box 65°C — Water 70°C

Which flask will cool fastest?
Give a reason for your answer.

Flask .... will cool fastest because ....

....

....

Q7 Mr Green makes a **solar hot water panel** from an old white central heating radiator made of **steel**.

wooden support

old radiator

wooden roof

Mr Green fixes the panel to the roof of his garden shed. Sadly, he finds that the water does not get very hot, even on sunny days.

air space

Explain how Mr Green could improve the design of his solar hot water panel.

pipes connected to hot water tank and pump

....

....

....

....

Kinetic Theory

Q1 The pictures below show the arrangement of particles in a solid, a liquid and a gas. Draw lines to match each picture and description to the correct word.

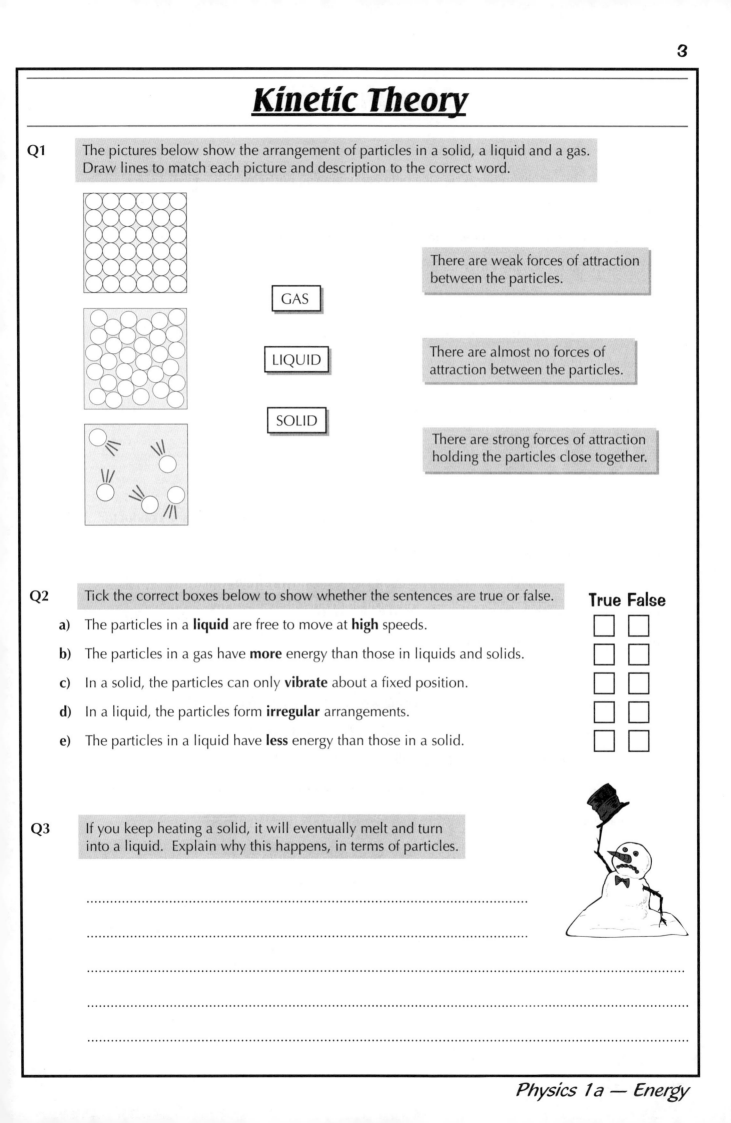

GAS

LIQUID

SOLID

There are weak forces of attraction between the particles.

There are almost no forces of attraction between the particles.

There are strong forces of attraction holding the particles close together.

Q2 Tick the correct boxes below to show whether the sentences are true or false.

True False

a) The particles in a **liquid** are free to move at **high** speeds. ☐ ☐

b) The particles in a gas have **more** energy than those in liquids and solids. ☐ ☐

c) In a solid, the particles can only **vibrate** about a fixed position. ☐ ☐

d) In a liquid, the particles form **irregular** arrangements. ☐ ☐

e) The particles in a liquid have **less** energy than those in a solid. ☐ ☐

Q3 If you keep heating a solid, it will eventually melt and turn into a liquid. Explain why this happens, in terms of particles.

....

....

....

....

....

Conduction

Q1 Tick to show whether the sentences below are true or false.

True False

a) Conduction involves **energy** passing between **vibrating particles**. ☐ ☐

b) Some **metals** are very **poor** conductors. ☐ ☐

c) **Solids** are usually better **conductors** of heat than liquids and gases. ☐ ☐

d) **Conduction** is usually **faster** in **denser solids**. ☐ ☐

Q2 George picks up a piece of wood and a metal spoon. Both have the same temperature: 20 °C.

Explain why the metal spoon feels **colder** to the touch than the piece of wood.

....

....

Q3 For each of the descriptions below, say whether it describes an **insulator** or a **conductor**.

a) There are **large** spaces between the particles. ....

b) Heat transfer is **quick** because the particles in the material **collide** a lot. ....

c) Some types of these materials contain **free electrons**. ....

d) The particles are **close** together. ....

Q4 Sajid, Mamphela and Ruth are discussing why copper is a good conductor of heat.

Sajid says, "**Copper is a great conductor because it's got electrons in it.**"

Mamphela says, "**It conducts well because it's shiny.**"

Ruth says, "**It conducts well because all its particles have kinetic energy.**"

Each pupil has made at least one mistake. Explain one mistake made by:

a) Sajid ....

....

b) Mamphela ....

....

c) Ruth ....

....

Convection

Q1 a) Tick the boxes next to the sentences to show whether they are true or false.

True False

   i) In a hot water tank, an immersion heater is usually placed at the bottom of the tank.

   ii) The hotter the water, the denser it is.

   iii) Convection currents happen when hot water displaces cold water.

   iv) Convection currents can happen in water but not in air.

b) Write a correction for each false sentence.

....

....

....

Q2 Match each observation with an explanation.

The very bottom of a hot water tank stays cold...

because water doesn't conduct much heat.

Warm air rises...

because heat flows from warm places to cooler ones.

A small heater can send heat all over a room...

because it is not so dense.

Q3 The picture below shows a radiator being used to heat up a room.

a) What happens to the **energy** of the particles in the air next to the radiator? Explain your answer.

....

....

....

b) Briefly explain how the change in the particles' energy causes a convection current in the room.

....

....

....

6

Convection

Q4 Convection can make water flow round the pipes in a house, without using a pump. Miss Jenkins demonstrates this to her pupils using the apparatus below.

glass tube filled with cold water

potassium permanganate crystals

a) Draw arrows on the diagram to show which way the water moves.

b) Explain what happens to the water above the heat to cause the convection current.

....

....

....

....

....

Q5 Sam uses the apparatus shown to investigate heat transfer in water.

Ice floating at the top

He heats the middle of the tube with a Bunsen flame. The ice at the top of the tube melts quickly, but the ice at the bottom does not melt.

Glass tube full of cold water

What does this experiment show about conduction and convection in water? Explain your answer.

Ice weighted so it stays at the bottom

....

....

....

Top Tips: Remember, convection only happens in fluids (liquids and gases), conduction happens fastest in solids, but all objects emit and absorb heat radiation.

Condensation and Evaporation

Q1 Complete the passage using the words given below. You will not have to use all the words.

kinetic energy   heats up   liquid   attractive   light energy   solid   repulsive   cools

Condensation is when a gas turns into a .... As a gas

....................................., the particles in the gas slow down and lose ....

The particles are pulled closer together by the .... forces between the

particles. If the particles get close enough together, then condensation takes place.

Q2 a) Tick the boxes to show whether the sentences are true or false.

True False

   i) Evaporation is when particles escape from a liquid. ☐ ☐

   ii) Particles can only evaporate from a liquid at temperatures above the liquid's boiling point. ☐ ☐

   iii) Only the speed of a particle affects whether it can escape a liquid. ☐ ☐

b) Write a correction for each false sentence.

....

....

Q3 Explain why your body **sweats more** when you do exercise or get hot. You should talk about particles in your answer.

....

....

....

....

....

Q4 List **two** factors that would **increase** the **rate** of each of the following:

a) evaporation of a liquid.

....

....

b) condensation of a gas.

....

....

Rate of Heat Transfer

Q1   Radiators are used to transfer heat to their surroundings.

a)   Why do radiators have a large surface area?

....

b)   Explain why a radiator would transfer heat quicker to a **metal spoon**
in contact with it, than to the **air** surrounding it.

....

....

Q2   List four features of a **vacuum flask** that reduce non-useful heat transfers.
State whether each reduces conduction, convection or radiation.

1...

2...

3...

4...

Plastic cap
filled with
cork

Shiny
mirrored
surfaces

Vacuum

Sponge

Air

Plastic case

Q3   Mr Pink has a copper hot water tank with an electric **immersion heater** in it.
The hot water tank **loses heat** from its **walls** by radiation, conduction and convection.
Complete the table below, showing how to **reduce non-useful** heat transfers from the tank's walls.

Type of Transfer	Suggested improvements to reduce heat loss
Radiation	
Conduction	
Convection	

Which fluid will move and carry heat away?
Where will it go, and how could you stop it?

Rate of Heat Transfer

Q4 Humans and animals have ways to help them control their heat transfer.

a) Explain why the hairs on your skin 'stand up' when you're cold.

....

....

b) Explain why some people's skin goes pink when they're hot.

....

....

Q5 The picture shows two different types of fox.

Fox A

Fox B

a) Identify which fox lives in a cold Arctic region and which lives in a desert.

i) Fox A .... ii) Fox B ....

b) Explain how the difference in the size of the ears of the two foxes helps each of them to survive in its natural habitat.

....

....

....

Q6 Hayley measured some cubes to find out their surface area to volume ratio. Her results are shown in the table.

Length of cube side (cm)	Surface area of cube (cm^2)	Volume of cube (cm^3)	Surface area: volume ratio
2	24	8	
4	96	64	
6	216	216	
8	384	512	
10	600	1000	

a) Calculate the **surface area : volume ratio** for each cube and write your answers in the table. *Just divide the surface area by the volume.*

b) As the cube size becomes larger, what happens to the value of the **surface area : volume ratio**?

....

c) Would you expect the smallest cube (length 2 cm) or the largest cube (length 10 cm) to change temperature more quickly? Explain your answer.

....

d) Use your answers above to explain why car engines often have 'fins'.

....

....

Energy Efficiency in the Home

Q1   Heat is lost from a house through its **roof**, **walls**, **doors** and **windows**.

through the roof

....

....

through the doors

....

through the walls

....

....

....

a)   In the spaces on the diagram, write down at least one measure that could be taken to reduce heat losses through each part of the house.

b)   Miss Golightly has just bought a new house which has very large windows.
Suggest three ways she could reduce heat loss through the windows of her new house.

1.   ....

2.   ....

3.   ....

Q2   Explain how the following types of insulation work.

a)   Cavity wall insulation ....

....

b)   Loft insulation ....

....

Top Tips: If you want to build a new house, there are regulations about making it energy efficient — that's one reason why a lot of new houses have quite small windows. If you live in an old house, you can sometimes get a grant to cover the cost of installing extra insulation.

Energy Efficiency in the Home

Q3 Mr Tarantino wants to buy **double glazing** for his house, but the salesman tries to sell him insulated window shutters instead. He says it is cheaper and more **cost-effective**.

	Double glazing	Insulated window shutters
Initial Cost	£3000	£1200
Annual Saving	£60	£20
Payback time	50 years	

a) Calculate the **payback time** for insulated shutters and write it in the table.

b) Is the salesman's advice correct? Give reasons for your answer.

....

....

Q4 Gary is choosing between two brands of loft insulation material.
Brand A has a U-value of 0.15 W/m²K. Brand B has a U-value of 0.2 W/m²K.

a) What do U-values measure?

....

b) If both brands are the same price, which brand should Gary buy? Explain your answer.

....

....

Q5 Shona, Tim, Meena and Alison are discussing what 'cost-effectiveness' means.

Cost-effectiveness means having a short payback time.

Cost-effectiveness means getting good value for your money.

Cost-effectiveness means getting a job done for a low price.

Cost-effectiveness just means not wasting energy.

Shona **Alison** **Tim** **Meena**

a) Whose explanations do you think are right? Circle their names.

Shona   Alison   Tim   Meena

b) Explain why the method with the shortest payback time is **not** always the best one to choose.

....

....

....

Specific Heat Capacity

Q1 a) What is **specific heat capacity**?

....

b) Agatha has 1 kg samples of two substances — A and B. Substance **A** has a **higher** specific heat capacity than substance B. Both samples cool down by 10 °C. Which will release more heat — A or B? Circle the correct answer.

Substance A

Substance B

Q2 To the right is a table with a list of **materials** and their **specific heat capacities**. Use the information in the table to help you answer the questions below.

Material	Specific heat capacity (J/kg°C)
Concrete	880
Oil	2000
Mercury	139
Water	4200
Copper	380

a) Which of the materials is used in storage heaters?

....

b) Which material is usually used to transfer heat around central heating systems? Explain why this material is the best one to use.

....

....

Q3 Mildred thinks she could make her hot water bottle more efficient by filling it with **mercury**, which has a specific heat capacity of **139 J/kg°C** . The specific heat capacity of water is **4200 J/kg°C**.

Work out the **difference** in energy released by two litres of mercury cooling from 70 °C to 20 °C and two litres of water cooling from 70 °C to 20 °C. (2 l of mercury has a mass of 27.2 kg. 2 l of water has a mass of 2 kg.)

Don't try this at home — mercury's toxic at any temperature.

....

....

....

Q4 A piece of copper is heated to **90 °C** and then lowered into a beaker of water which is at **20 °C**. The copper transfers **3040 J** of energy to the water before it is removed. The temperature of the copper after it is removed is **50 °C**. The specific heat capacity of copper is **380 J/kg°C**.

Calculate the **mass** of the copper. ....

....

....

Energy Transfer

Q1 Use the words below to fill in the gaps.

  dissipated   transferred   created   conservation

The Principle for the .... of Energy says:

Energy can be .... usefully from one form to another, stored or

.... — but it can never be .... or destroyed.

Q2 Complete the following **energy transfer diagrams**. The first one has been done for you.

A solar water heating panel: ....light energy............... → ....heat energy...............

a) A gas cooker: .... → heat and light energy

b) An electric buzzer: ....electrical energy........... → ....

c) A television screen: .... → ....

Q3 The diagram shows a **steam locomotive**.

a) What form(s) of energy are there in the:

i) coal ....

ii) hot steam (which powers the engine) ....

b) Describe two **energy transfers** which take place on the locomotive.

1...

2...

Oil lamp   Coal

Q4 Bruce is practising weightlifting.

a) When Bruce holds the bar still, above his head, what kind of energy does the weight have?

....

b) Bruce had porridge for breakfast. Describe how the chemical energy in his porridge is transferred into the energy of the weight identified in part a).

....

....

c) When Bruce lets go of the weight, what happens to its energy?

....

Energy Transfer

Q5   For each of the electrical appliances below, draw a line
to the form of useful energy it is designed to produce.

electrical energy

Electric Fan

heat energy

Iron

kinetic energy

Bedside table lamp

sound energy

light energy

CGP's biggest fan

Q6   When an archer shoots an arrow into the air several **energy transfers** take place.
The table below shows these transformations, but in the wrong order.
Number the energy transformations from 1 to 5 to show the correct order.

Order	Energy transfers
	Energy stored in the pulled bow and string is transferred into kinetic energy.
	The arrow loses gravitational potential energy and gains kinetic energy as it falls to earth.
	Chemical energy in the archer's muscles is transferred into elastic potential energy.
1	Chemical energy from the archer's food is stored in his muscles.
	As it goes upwards the arrow loses kinetic energy and gains gravitational potential energy.

Q7   Each of the following sentences is incorrect. Write a correct version of each one.

a)   In a battery-powered torch, the battery transfers **electrical energy** into **light energy**.

....

b)   A **wind turbine** transfers **kinetic energy** into **electrical energy** only.

....

c)   A wind-up toy car transfers **chemical energy** into **kinetic energy** and **sound energy**.

....

Q8   Write down the name of an appliance which transfers:

a)   electrical energy into **sound energy** ....

b)   light energy into **electrical energy** ....

c)   electrical energy into **heat** and **kinetic energy** ....

Efficiency of Machines

Q1   Fill in the gaps using the correct words from the list below.

heat   light   input   create   output   total   useful   fraction   transfer
A **machine** is a device which can .... energy. Some of the energy
supplied to the machine is transferred into .... output energy.
But some energy is always wasted — often as .... or sound energy.
The **efficiency** of a **machine** is the .... of the **total energy**
.... that is transferred into useful energy ....

Q2   Here is an **energy flow diagram** for an electric lamp. Complete the following sentences.

100 J Energy Input

5 J Light Energy

Heat Energy

a)   The **total energy input** is .... J

b)   The **useful energy output** is .... J

c)   The amount of energy **wasted** is .... J

Q3   Complete the table below.

Appliance	Total Energy Input (J)	Useful Energy Output (J)	Efficiency
1	2000	1500	
2		2000	0.50
3	4000		0.25

Q4   A kettle has a power rating of 2000 W.
If it's 90% efficient, calculate its useful power output.

....

....

....

Efficiency of Machines

Q5 Tina was investigating a model **winch** —
a machine that uses an electric motor to lift objects.

Tina calculated that, in theory, **10 J** of electrical energy would be needed
to lift a **boot** 50 cm off a table. She then tried lifting the boot with the
winch, and found that, actually, **20 J** of electrical energy was used.

Why did the winch use so much more electrical energy in practice?
In your answer, include an explanation of what happened to the 'extra' 10 joules.

....

....

....

....

Q6 Sajid hopes his new MP3 player is better than his old one.
He decides to test which one is more **efficient**. He puts new
batteries in both MP3 players and switches them on. Then he
times how long they each play for before the batteries run out.

a) How can he compare the **useful energy outputs**?

....

....

....

....

b) Write down two things Sajid must do to make it a **fair test**.

....

....

c) Player A lasts for 3 hours and Player B lasts for 4 hours.
Write a **conclusion** for Sajid's experiment.

....

....

....

Efficiency of Machines

Q7 Cars use **heat exchangers** to use some of the 'waste' heat energy produced by the car's engine.

Describe **one** way this heat energy can be used.

....

....

....

Q8 Clive is researching different kinds of electric light bulb. He finds the following information.

	Low-energy bulb	Ordinary bulb
Electrical energy input per second (J)	15	60
Light energy output per second (J)	1.4	1.4
Cost	£3.50	50p
Typical expected lifetime	8 years	1 year
Estimated annual running cost	£1.00	£4.00

Hint — most people don't like wasting money.

a) Write down two reasons for choosing a **low-energy** light bulb.

1) ....

2) ....

b) Write down two reasons why Clive might prefer to buy an ordinary bulb.

1) ....

2) ....

Top Tips: So... efficiency = good, waste = bad. Got it? Good. Remember — there's always a sneaky bit of waste energy produced by all machines, so nothing is 100% efficient. Some machines have heat exchangers to use wasted heat energy to do other things — clever, huh?

Energy Transformation Diagrams

Q1 This diagram shows the energy changes in a **toy crane**. The diagram is drawn to scale.

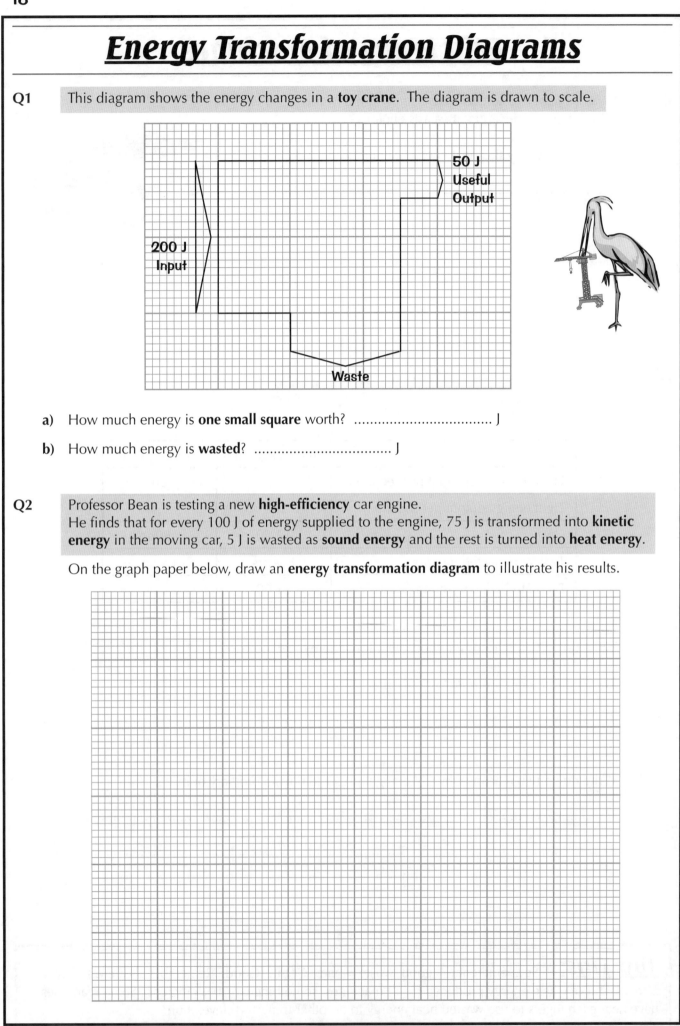

a) How much energy is **one small square** worth? .... J

b) How much energy is **wasted**? .... J

Q2 Professor Bean is testing a new **high-efficiency** car engine.
He finds that for every 100 J of energy supplied to the engine, 75 J is transformed into **kinetic energy** in the moving car, 5 J is wasted as **sound energy** and the rest is turned into **heat energy**.

On the graph paper below, draw an **energy transformation diagram** to illustrate his results.

Energy Transformation Diagrams

Q3 Liam measured the energy input and outputs for a model **electrical generator**.
He drew this diagram to show his results.

Describe two mistakes Liam has made on his diagram, and suggest how to correct them.

1...

....

....

2..

....

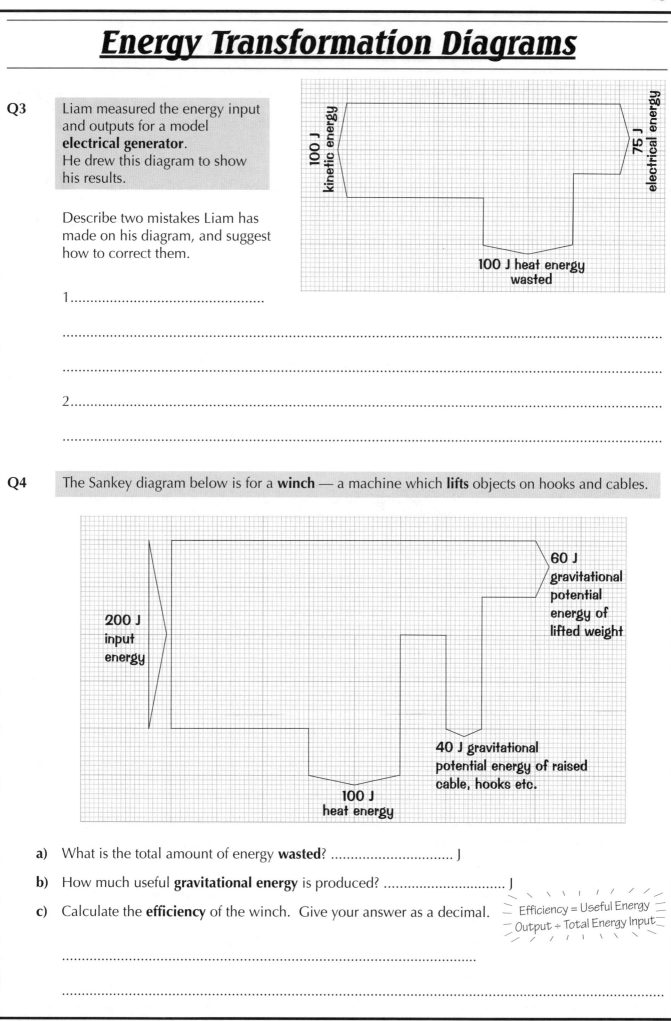

100 J kinetic energy

75 J electrical energy

100 J heat energy wasted

Q4 The Sankey diagram below is for a **winch** — a machine which **lifts** objects on hooks and cables.

200 J input energy

60 J gravitational potential energy of lifted weight

40 J gravitational potential energy of raised cable, hooks etc.

100 J heat energy

a) What is the total amount of energy **wasted**? .... J

b) How much useful **gravitational energy** is produced? .... J

c) Calculate the **efficiency** of the winch. Give your answer as a decimal.

Efficiency = Useful Energy Output ÷ Total Energy Input

....

....

The Cost of Electricity

Q1   Boris puts his **2 kW** electric heater on for 3 hours.

    a) Calculate how many **kilowatt-hours** of electrical energy the heater uses.

        Energy used = ...

    b) Boris gets his electricity supply from Ivasparkco. They charge 14p per kilowatt-hour.
        Work out the **cost** of the energy calculated in part (a).

....

....

Q2   Tick the box next to the correct cost of using a **100 W** lamp
for **10 hours**, if electrical energy costs **11.3p per kWh**.

You need to turn 100 W into kilowatts first.

    ☐ £1.13   ☐ 22.6p   ☐ 11.3p

Q3   Tina's mum grumbles at her for leaving a 60 W lamp on overnight — about 9 hours every night.
Tina says her mum uses **more energy** by using an 8 kW shower for 15 minutes every day.

Is Tina right? Calculate how much energy each person uses and compare your results.

....

....

....

....

Q4   Mr Havel recently received his electricity bill. Unfortunately,
he tore off the bottom part to write a shopping list.

    a) How many **kWh** of energy did Mr Havel use
        in the three months from June to September?

Customer : Havel, V	
Date	Meter Reading (kWh)
11 06 06	34259
10 09 06	34783
Total Cost @ 9.7p per kWh	

....

    b) What would the bill have said for 'total cost'?

....

....

The Cost of Electricity

Q5   **Pumped storage** power stations work by using **off-peak** electricity to pump water into a holding reservoir at night. In the daytime they release water from the reservoir to generate electricity, which is then sold to the National Grid at **peak rate** prices. The table below shows data for a typical pumped storage power station.

	Night time (input)	Daytime (output)
Running time	7 hours	5 hours
Power	275 MW	288 MW
Cost per kWh	3.7p	7.2p

Be careful — watch out for <u>units</u>.

a)   Calculate the cost of electricity used in the night time operation.

....

....

b)   Calculate the value (in £) of the electricity generated in the daytime operation.

....

....

Q6   Mr Macintosh wants to work out how much **energy** he could save if he turned all his electrical appliances off overnight, instead of leaving them on standby.

On Tuesday night, he leaves all his appliances on **standby**. He takes a meter reading at **9pm** before going to bed and at **9am** the next morning when he wakes up. On Thursday night he **repeats** the experiment, but this time he **turns off** all his appliances.

Tuesday:
Reading at 9pm

Wednesday:
Reading at 9am

Thursday:
Reading at 9pm

Friday:
Reading at 9am

`1 3 5 9 2 . 4 2` kWh   `1 3 5 9 8 . 6 3` kWh   `1 3 6 4 6 . 6 8` kWh   `1 3 6 4 9 . 4 1` kWh

Appliances on standby   *Appliances turned off*

Calculate the amount of energy Mr Macinstosh saved by turning off his electrical appliances overnight, rather than leaving them on standby.

....

....

....

Choosing Electrical Appliances

Q1 Two different types of power drill and some of their features are shown below.

Mains Powered Drill

Power output: 1.2 kW

Battery Powered Drill

Power output: 200 W

Battery Life: 8 hours

Suggest **two** reasons someone might choose to buy the battery
powered drill instead of the mains powered drill.

....

....

Q2 A **battery powered lamp** takes **6 hours** to charge fully when connected to
a **400 W** power supply. This gives the lamp enough energy for **8 hours** of use.
A **mains powered** lamp has a power rating of **1.6 kW**.

a) If both lamps are used for 8 hours, calculate the difference in the amount of energy used.
Give your answer in kWh.

....

....

....

b) If the cost of electricity is 12p per kWh, calculate the difference in cost of using both lamps for 8 hours.

....

c) Suggest why somebody going on a camping trip might choose to buy a wind-up lamp instead of the
mains powered or battery powered lamps described above.

....

....

Q3 **Access to electricity** can improve people's **standard of living** in developing countries.

Give two examples of how electricity can help improve **public health** in developing countries.

1. ....

2. ....

Mixed Questions — Physics 1a

Q1   Paul is looking to buy some cavity wall insulation to reduce heat loss from his house.

a)   Explain how cavity wall insulation works.

....

....

b)   Should Paul look for cavity wall insulation with a high or a low U-value? Explain your answer.

....

....

c)   Paul has noticed he often gets condensation on the inside of his windows.
He is considering whether to get them double glazed.

Explain in terms of particles why the condensation happens.

....

....

....

Q2   Ben sets up an experiment as shown. He records the temperature
readings on thermometers A and B every two minutes.

The graph below shows Ben's results
for thermometer **B**.

a)   On the diagram above, sketch the graph you would expect for thermometer **A**.

b)   Explain the differences between the two graphs.

....

....

....

c)   Complete the energy transfer diagram below for the Bunsen burner used in Ben's experiment.

....   →   ....

Mixed Questions — Physics 1a

Q3   Steve has bought a new fridge-freezer.

a)   Steve's new fridge-freezer has its freezer compartment above the refrigerator.
How does this arrangement encourage **convection currents** in the main body of the fridge?

....

....

b)   The fridge-freezer has a power of 500 W. Steve's electricity costs him 15p per kWh.
How much does it cost Steve to have the fridge-freezer switched on for a whole day (24 hours)?

....

....

....

Q4   Eric investigates ways of saving energy in his grandmother's house. He calculates the annual savings that could be made on his grandma's fuel bills, and the cost of doing the work.

Work needed	Annual Saving (£)	Cost of work (£)
Hot water tank jacket	15	15
Draught-proofing	65	70
Cavity wall insulation	70	560
Thermostatic controls	25	120

a)   Which of these energy-saving measures has the shortest **payback time**?

....

b)   Which of the options in the table would save Eric's grandma the most money **over 5 years**?
Show your working.

....

....

....

c)   Erik's grandma likes to have a hot bath in the evenings. How much energy is needed to heat 90 kg of water from 14 °C to 36 °C ? (The specific heat capacity of water is 4200 J/kg°C.)

....

....

....

Mixed Questions — Physics 1a

Q5 In one coal-fired power station, for every **1000 J** of energy input to the power station, 100 J is wasted in the **boiler**, 500 J is wasted in the **cooling water** and 50 J is wasted in the **generator**.

a) What **type** of energy is contained in the **coal**? ....

b) On the grid below, draw a detailed energy transformation diagram for this power station.

c) Calculate the **efficiency** of the power station.

....

....

Q6 Heat sinks are devices often used in computer circuits to transfer heat away from hot components.

a) Explain why heat sinks have **fins**.

....

....

b) Heat sinks are usually made of metal.

i) Why are metals **good conductors** of heat?

....

ii) Describe how heat is **transferred** from the hot end of a piece of metal to the cool end.

....

....

....

Energy Sources & Power Stations

Q1   In a coal-fired power station, there are several steps involved in making electricity. Number these steps in the right order.

☐   Hot steam rushes through a turbine and makes it spin.

☐   Electricity is produced by the spinning generator.

☐   Coal is burned to release heat.

☐   The spinning turbine makes the generator spin too.

☐   Water is heated in a boiler and turned to steam.

Q2   Nuclear power stations provide about 20% of the UK's electrical energy.

a)   How do uranium and plutonium provide heat energy?

....

b)   Uranium and plutonium are both non-renewable sources of energy. Explain what this means.

....

....

Q3   Use the words in the following list, to complete the paragraph below.

non-renewable   kinetic   chemical   electrical   fossil   heat

Most power stations use .... sources of energy, such as coal,

oil or gas. These .... fuels are initially burnt in a boiler.

This converts the .... energy in the fuel to .... energy.

A turbine then converts this energy into .... energy, which, in turn is

converted to .... energy by a generator.

This energy feeds into the national grid ready to be distributed to consumers.

Q4   Suggest a reason why wind and solar power are less reliable sources of energy than fossil fuels.

....

....

Top Tips: Make sure you know the difference between renewable and non-renewable energy sources, plus the different types of each. Then the exam will be a breeze — like wind through a turbine.

Renewable Energy Sources (1)

Q1 People often object to wind turbines being put up near to where they live.

a) List three reasons why they might object.

1)..

2)..

3)..

b) List three arguments in favour of using wind turbines to generate electricity.

1)..

2)..

3)..

Q2 Explain the advantages and disadvantages of using **solar cells** to generate electricity.

....

....

....

Q3 Renewable sources are often used for **small scale** production of electricity.

a) Explain why they're useful for this purpose.

....

....

b) A farmer on a remote farm uses a wind turbine to generate his electricity. He generates more electricity than he needs, and wants to connect his wind turbine to the national grid so he can sell his spare electricity. However, no electricity companies want to supply the connection and buy the excess energy. Suggest a reason for this.

....

....

Renewable Energy Sources (2)

Q1 Lynn and Hua are using the apparatus below to investigate how hydroelectric power works.

They put the tank at several different heights and recorded the voltage from the generator.

Height of tank (cm)	300	250	200	150	100
Voltage (V)	3.1	2.0	1.1	0.6	0.2
Brightness of lamp	bright	normal	dim	just lit	not lit

a) Why did they measure the **voltage** instead of just noting the brightness of the lamp?

....

b) They predicted that the energy generated would be **proportional** to the height of the tank. Do their results support this prediction? Explain your answer.

Their results **support / do not support** their prediction because ....

....

Q2 These sentences explain how pumped storage works. Put them in the right order by numbering them 1 to 4.

☐ Water at a high level stores energy until it is needed.

☐ At peak times, when demand is highest, water is allowed to flow downhill, powering turbines and generating electricity.

☐ At night big power stations make more electricity than is needed.

☐ Spare electricity is used to pump water from reservoirs at a low level to others at a high level.

Renewable Energy Sources (2)

Q3   Match up the beginnings and ends of the sentences. In one case, two matches are possible.

Big coal-fired power stations deliver energy...

when it is needed.

Pumped storage power stations deliver energy...

all the time.

Hydroelectric power stations deliver electricity...

that they have previously stored.

Q4   At a public meeting, people are sharing their views about hydroelectric power.

We should use hydroelectric power more — it doesn't cause any pollution.

And it gives us loads of free energy.

But it makes a terrible mess of the countryside.

At least it's reliable — it always gives us electricity when we need it.

Brian   **Hillary**   **Sue**   **Liz**

Say whether you agree or disagree with each person's view, and explain your reasons.

a)   I **agree** / **disagree** with Brian because ....

....

b)   I **agree** / **disagree** with Hillary because ....

....

c)   I **agree** / **disagree** with Sue because ....

....

d)   I **agree** / **disagree** with Liz because ....

....

e)   Outline two **advantages** of hydroelectric power which were not mentioned at the public meeting.

1)..

2)..

f)   Outline two **disadvantages** of hydroelectric power not mentioned at the meeting.

1)..

2)..

Renewable Energy Sources (3)

Q1 Tick the boxes to show whether each statement applies to **wave** power or **tidal** power or **both**.

Wave Tidal

a) Is usually used in estuaries. ☐ ☐

b) Suitable for small-scale use. ☐ ☐

c) Is a reliable way to generate electricity. ☐ ☐

d) The amount of energy generated depends on the weather. ☐ ☐

e) The amount of energy generated depends on the time of the month and year. ☐ ☐

Q2 **Tidal barrages** can be used to generate electricity.

What happens to make turbines go round?

a) Explain how a tidal barrage works.

....

....

....

b) Give two reasons why people might object to a tidal barrage being built.

1...

2...

Q3 **Wave-powered generators** can be very useful around islands, like Britain.

a) Number these sentences 1 to 6, to explain how a wave-powered generator works.

☐ The spinning generator makes electricity.

☐ The moving air makes the turbine spin.

☐ The water goes down again.

☐ Air is sucked downwards, spinning the turbine the other way and generating more power.

☐ A wave moves water upwards, forcing air out towards a turbine.

☐ The spinning turbine drives a generator.

b) Give two possible problems with using wave power.

1...

2...

Physics 1b — Electricity and Waves

Renewable Energy Sources (4)

Q1   Use the words below to complete the following paragraph.

woodchips   fossil fuels   ethanol   water

steam   turbines   methane

Biofuels are used to generate electricity in a similar way to ....

Biofuels are burnt to heat .... and make .... which is used

to drive .... to power generators and make electricity.

Biofuels can be solids (e.g. ....), liquids (e.g. ....) or

gases (e.g. ....).

Q2   Describe how electricity is generated using geothermal energy.

....

....

....

Q3   Explain why biofuels are a 'renewable' source of energy.

....

....

Q4   Tick the boxes to show whether these statements about **geothermal** energy are true or false.

True   False

a)   Set-up costs are low.   ☐ ☐

b)   It is possible in any country in the world.   ☐ ☐

c)   There are lots of associated environmental problems.   ☐ ☐

d)   Geothermal power stations use steam to drive turbines.   ☐ ☐

Top Tips: Biofuels and geothermal energy are both renewable energy sources. One is steam coming from underground, and the other is burning stuff like wood and cow muck. How lovely.

32

Energy Sources and the Environment

Q1 Draw lines to match up each environmental problem below with something that causes it.

Acid rain

Climate change

Dangerous radioactive waste

Spoiling of natural landscapes

Releasing CO_2 by burning fossil fuels

Coal mining

Sulfur dioxide formed by burning oil and coal

Using nuclear power

Q2 Lisa says: "Using nuclear power to make electricity is too dangerous."
Ben says: "Using fossil fuels is even more dangerous in the long run."

Who do you think is right? Explain your answer.

....

....

....

Q3 Biofuels are often described as being 'carbon neutral'.

Explain why burning biofuels is 'carbon neutral'.

....

....

....

Q4 'Carbon capture' reduces the impact of burning fossil fuels on the environment.

a) Describe what is meant by the term 'carbon capture'?

....

....

b) Give an example of how the captured carbon dioxide can be stored.

....

Physics 1b — Electricity and Waves

Comparison of Energy Resources

Q1   Which of the following fossil fuel power stations has the shortest start-up time? Circle your answer.

Coal   Oil   Gas

Q2   The city of Fakeville decides to replace its old coal-fired power station.
They have to choose between using gas, nuclear, wind or geothermal.

Give one **disadvantage** of each choice:

a)   **Gas** ....

....

b)   **Nuclear** ....

....

c)   **Wind** ....

....

d)   **Geothermal** ....

....

Q3   This is part of a leaflet produced by the pressure group 'Nuclear Is Not the Answer' (NINA).

Read the extract and answer the questions on the next page.

Imagine life without electricity. No lights, no computers, no TV… no kettles, no tea? Unthinkable.
But that's what could happen when the oil and gas run out — because in the UK we generate about
75% of our electricity from power stations running on fossil fuels.

The Government has decided to build more nuclear power stations.
At NINA, we believe that nuclear is not the answer.

Nuclear power stations generate power, yes, but they also generate huge piles of highly radioactive
waste. No one has any idea how to get rid of this waste safely. So should we really be making more
of it? Radioactive waste stays dangerous for hundreds of thousands of years. Would you be happy
living near a nuclear fuel dump? That's not all — nuclear power stations, and the lethal waste they
create, are obvious targets for terrorists. And, last but not least, building more nuclear power stations
would cost the taxpayer billions.

The good news is, we don't need nuclear power. There are safer, cleaner ways to produce electricity
— using renewable energy. Many people argue that renewables are unreliable — the wind doesn't
always blow, for instance. Well, true, but tidal power is reliable —
and we have hundreds of miles of coastline with tides washing in and out twice every day.

If you don't want your children to grow up in a nuclear-powered world, join NINA today.

Comparison of Energy Resources

a) Explain clearly why the author thinks that we could find ourselves without electricity.

....

....

b) Give two reasons why the author thinks nuclear power is **dangerous**.

1...

2...

c) Nuclear power stations are the most expensive type of power plant to **decommission**.

Explain what is meant by the term decommission.

....

....

d) The author suggests that tidal power is a **plentiful** and **reliable** source of energy. Do you agree? Explain your answer.

I **agree** / **disagree** because ....

....

....

e) Give two possible arguments **in favour** of nuclear power.

1...

....

2...

....

Electricity and the National Grid

Q1 Number these statements 1 to 5 to show the order of the steps that are needed to deliver energy to Mrs Miggins' house so that she can boil the kettle.

	An electrical current flows through power cables across the country.
	Mrs Miggins boils the kettle for tea.
	Electrical energy is generated in power stations.
	The voltage of the supply is raised.
	The voltage of the supply is reduced.

Q2 Electricity can be transmitted by either **overhead** or **underground cables**.
Tick the appropriate box to answer each of the following questions:

	Overhead cables	Underground cables
a) Which **cost** more to set up?	☐	☐
b) Which require the most **maintenance**?	☐	☐
c) Which are the easiest to **repair**?	☐	☐
d) Which are most affected by **weather**?	☐	☐
e) Which are most **reliable**?	☐	☐
f) Which are the **easiest** to install?	☐	☐
g) Which cause the most disturbance to **land**?	☐	☐

Q3 Using **high voltages** in power cables means you need some **expensive** equipment.

a) Make a list of the main equipment you need for **high voltage transmission**.

....

....

b) Explain why it is still **cheaper** to use **high voltages** for transmission.

....

....

Top Tips: Wowsers. Overhead and underground cables are pretty darn interesting. Or maybe not. Either way, you need to know the pros and cons of both types of cable, soz.

Electricity and the National Grid

Q4   Each of the following sentences is incorrect.
Write a correct version of each.

a)   The National Grid transmits energy at **high voltage** and **high current**.

....

b)   A step-up transformer is used to **reduce the voltage** of the supply before electricity is transmitted.

....

c)   Using a **high current** makes sure there is not much energy **wasted**.

....

Q5   The **National Grid** distributes
electricity from power stations
to the consumers.

a)   Explain what is meant by the 'supply and demand' of electricity.

....

....

b)   Describe **one** problem the National Grid faces concerning supply and demand.

....

c)   Suggest **two** ways the National Grid can increase the supply of electricity.

....

....

d)   Suggest **two** ways in which consumers can help reduce demand for electricity.

....

....

Top Tips: The key thing to remember is that high voltage means low current, which means
the cables don't get so hot — so less energy is wasted. And while you're at it, the ways of matching
supply with demand are really important to learn too. You might get asked about all this stuff in the
exam, which is why we put it in our book. It wasn't just for fun. If you did have fun — good for you.

Wave Basics

Q1 Complete the sentence below by circling the correct word in each pair.

Waves transfer **energy / matter** without transferring any **energy / matter**.

Q2 There are **two ways** in which you can make waves on a **slinky** spring.

a) Which diagram shows a **transverse** wave, and which one shows a **longitudinal** wave?

Transverse: ....

Longitudinal: ....

b) Write down one difference between these two types of wave.

....

....

Q3 Diagrams **A**, **B** and **C** represent electromagnetic waves.

A   **B**   **C**

a) Which two diagrams show waves with the same **frequency**?   .... and ....

b) Which two diagrams show waves with the same **amplitude**?   .... and ....

c) Which two diagrams show waves with the same **wavelength**?   .... and ....

Q4 Which of the phrases below relate to **transverse** waves and which to **longitudinal**?
Write 'T' for transverse, and 'L' for longitudinal.

☐ vibrations are at 90° to the direction of energy transfer   ☐ electromagnetic radiation

☐ sound waves   ☐ vibrations are along the same direction as the energy transfer

☐ produced by a slinky spring whose end is wiggled at 90° to the spring itself   ☐ ripples on water   ☐ produced by a slinky spring whose end is pushed and pulled towards and away from the rest of the spring

Wave Basics

Q5   All waves have a **frequency** and a **wavelength**.

a)   What units are used to measure wavelength? ....

b)   What does it mean to say that "the frequency of a wave is 25 hertz"?

....

c)   The diagram shows a waveform.
Which of A, B or C is the length of one whole wave?

....

Q6   There are six equations below, some of which are **incorrect**.
Draw a big thick line through the ones that are incorrect.

$$\text{Frequency} = \text{Speed} \times \text{Wavelength}$$

$$\text{Frequency} = \frac{\text{Wavelength}}{\text{Speed}}$$

$$\text{Wavelength} = \frac{\text{Speed}}{\text{Frequency}}$$

$$\text{Speed} = \frac{\text{Frequency}}{\text{Wavelength}}$$

$$\text{Speed} = \text{Frequency} \times \text{Wavelength}$$

$$\text{Frequency} = \frac{\text{Speed}}{\text{Wavelength}}$$

Q7   **Green light** travels at 3×10^8 m/s and has a wavelength of about 5×10^{-7} m.

Calculate the **frequency** of green light. Give the correct unit in your answer.

....

....

Q8   Jason draws the graph on the right to show a wave
with an **amplitude** of **4 m** and a **wavelength** of **2 m**.

a)   What has Jason done wrong?

....

....

b)   On the same set of axes, draw a wave with a **wavelength**
of **5 m** and an **amplitude** of **3 m**.

Q9   An ultraviolet wave has a frequency of 4.6×10^{15} Hz. It travels at a speed of 3×10^8 m/s.

Calculate the **wavelength** of the wave.

....

....

Wave Properties

Q1   Harriet spends at least an hour looking at herself in a **mirror** every day.
The image she sees is formed from light reflected by the mirror.

a)   What is meant by a "normal" when talking about reflection?

....

....

b)   Complete the diagram to show an
incident ray of light being reflected
by the mirror. Label the **angle of
incidence**, **i**, the **normal**, and
the **angle of reflection**, **r**.

Mirror

Q2   The diagram below shows a pencil being reflected in a **plane mirror**.
Some of the rays have already been drawn in.

a)   On the diagram, draw in the rays
showing how light is reflected to form
an image of the **top** of the pencil.

mirror

b)   Is the image in a plane mirror real or virtual? ....

c)   Is the image inverted or upright? ....

d)   The image of the pencil is **laterally inverted**. Explain what this means.

....

....

Top Tips: If you get asked a question about constructing ray diagrams, remember the
important rule for drawing reflections in a plane mirror: **angle of incidence = angle of reflection**.
Always use a **ruler** to draw your ray diagrams too — examiners love a line drawn with a ruler.

Refraction and Diffraction

Q1   Waves can be **diffracted**.

a)   Explain what 'diffraction' means.

....

....

b)   A ripple tank is used to study the behaviour of waves as they pass through gaps. The gap in diagram 1 is about the **same size** as the wavelength. The gap in diagram 2 is **much bigger**. Complete both diagrams to show what happens to the waves after they pass through the gaps.

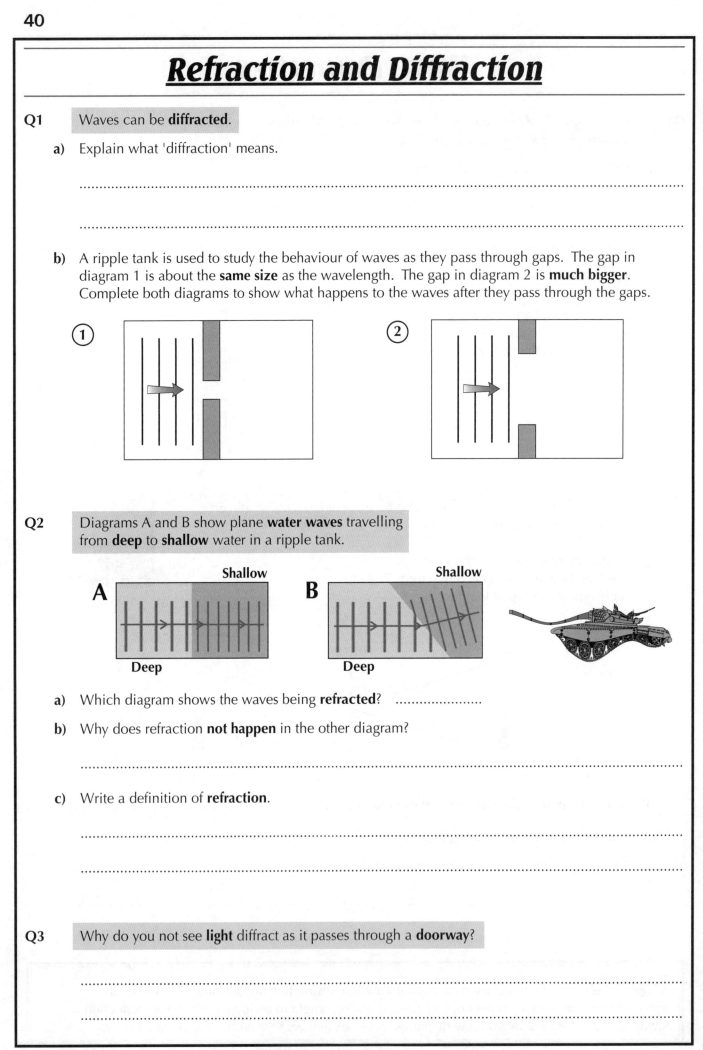

Q2   Diagrams A and B show plane **water waves** travelling from **deep** to **shallow** water in a ripple tank.

a)   Which diagram shows the waves being **refracted**?   ....

b)   Why does refraction **not happen** in the other diagram?

....

c)   Write a definition of **refraction**.

....

....

Q3   Why do you not see **light** diffract as it passes through a **doorway**?

....

....

EM Waves and Communication

Q1 The different types of **EM waves** form a spectrum.

a) Use the words below to complete the table to show the seven types of EM waves:

Infrared   Gamma rays   Ultraviolet
X-rays   Radio waves   Microwaves

			VISIBLE LIGHT			
1 m-10^4 m	10^{-2} m (1 cm)	10^{-5} m (0.01 mm)	10^{-7} m	10^{-8} m	10^{-10} m	10^{-15} m

b) In which direction does the **energy** of the electromagnetic radiation **increase** across the table? Tick the box next to the correct answer.

☐ The energy of the waves **increases** from **left to right** across the table.

☐ The energy of the waves **increases** from **right to left** across the table.

Q2 a) Tick the correct boxes to show whether each of the following statements is true or false.

True False

i) Visible light travels faster in a vacuum than both X-rays and radio waves. ☐ ☐

ii) All EM waves transfer matter from place to place. ☐ ☐

iii) Radio waves have the shortest wavelength of all EM waves. ☐ ☐

iv) All EM waves can travel through space. ☐ ☐

b) Write a correction for each false sentence.

....

....

....

....

Q3 Circle the letter next to the statements below that are true.

A Long waves such as radio waves are good for transmitting information long distances.

B Some wavelengths of radio wave are reflected by the ionosphere and come back to Earth.

C Short-wave radio waves can be diffracted around hills.

D To receive TV signals, you must be in the direct line of sight of the transmitter.

EM Waves and Communication

Q4 Complete the sentences below by circling the correct word in each pair.

EM waves with higher frequencies have **shorter / longer** wavelengths.

The **higher / lower** the frequency of an EM wave, the greater the energy of the wave.

Q5 The house shown below receives radio signals from a nearby transmitter, even though there is a mountain between the house and the transmitter.

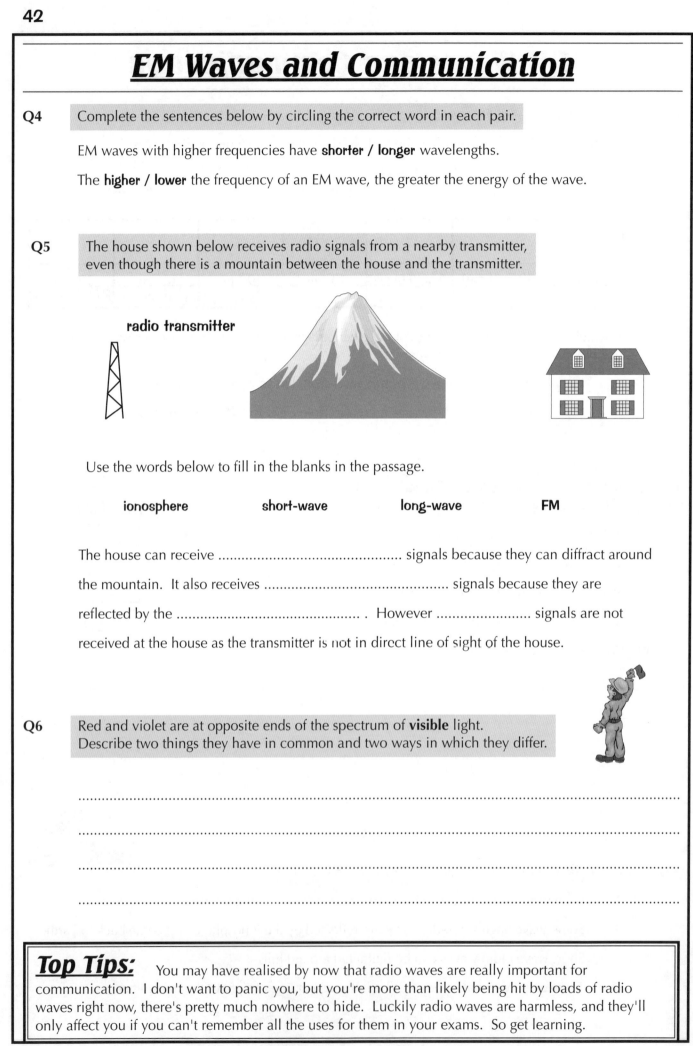

radio transmitter

Use the words below to fill in the blanks in the passage.

ionosphere **short-wave** **long-wave** **FM**

The house can receive .... signals because they can diffract around

the mountain. It also receives .... signals because they are

reflected by the .... However .... signals are not

received at the house as the transmitter is not in direct line of sight of the house.

Q6 Red and violet are at opposite ends of the spectrum of **visible** light.
Describe two things they have in common and two ways in which they differ.

....

....

....

....

EM Waves and Their Uses

Q1 Television remote controls use EM waves to communicate with the TV.

Underline the type of radiation used in wireless remote controls.

| Gamma | UV | Infrared | X-ray |

Q2 Gabrielle in Britain and Carwyn in Canada are talking by mobile phone.

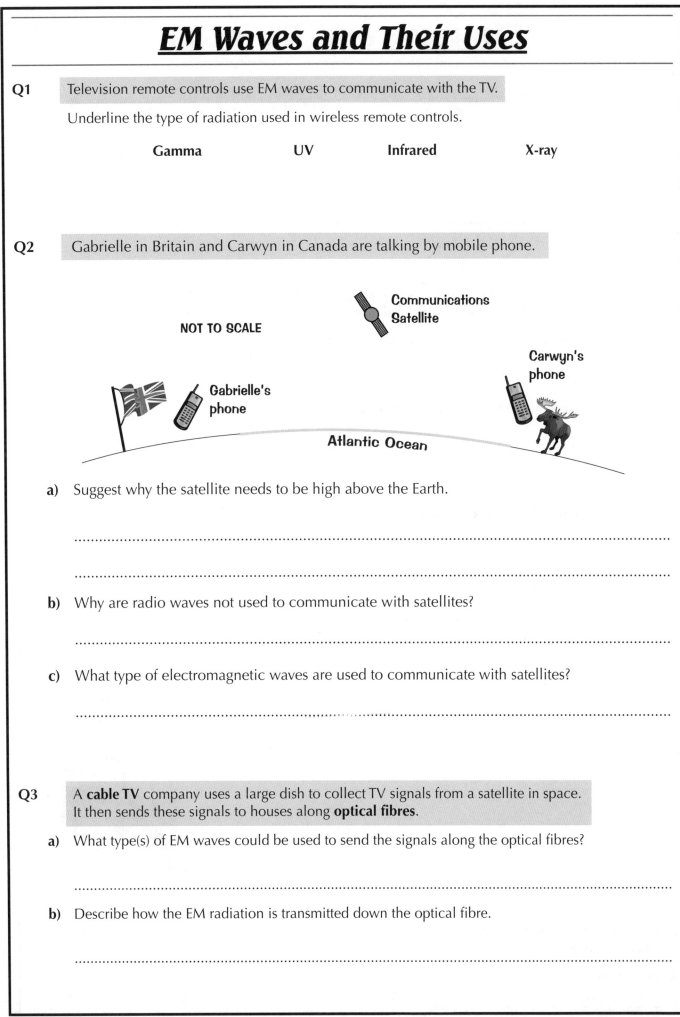

a) Suggest why the satellite needs to be high above the Earth.

....

....

b) Why are radio waves not used to communicate with satellites?

....

c) What type of electromagnetic waves are used to communicate with satellites?

....

Q3 A **cable TV** company uses a large dish to collect TV signals from a satellite in space. It then sends these signals to houses along **optical fibres**.

a) What type(s) of EM waves could be used to send the signals along the optical fibres?

....

b) Describe how the EM radiation is transmitted down the optical fibre.

....

44

44

EM Waves and Their Uses

Q4   Explain how a microwave camera on a remote-sensing satellite can 'see' through clouds.

....

....

....

Q5   It has been suggested that using **mobile phones** could cause **brain tumours**. However, at the moment there is **no reliable evidence** to prove that this is or isn't the case.

a)   What type of radiation is used by mobile phones?

....

b)   What could happen to the **brain cells** of people who use mobile phones?

....

....

c)   Why do people still **take the risk** by using mobile phones?

....

....

....

Q6   Visible light is used for photography.

Briefly describe how a camera uses visible light to take a photo.

....

....

....

Top Tips: There are four main types of electromagnetic radiation used in communications technology — microwaves, radio waves, visible light and infrared radiation. Make sure you know the uses of each. Then as a reward, practice using infrared radiation by channel hopping with your remote.

Sound Waves

Q1   Sound waves are caused by **vibrations**.

Put the following sentences in the correct order to describe how the sound of a drumbeat is made and reaches our ears.

A   The vibration of the drum sets the air molecules next to it vibrating too.

B   We hear the sound when the vibrations in the air reach our ears.

C   When someone beats a drum, the skin on top of the drum vibrates.

D   A series of compressions and decompressions travel outwards through the air (or other medium) as a longitudinal wave.

Correct order: .... , ... , ... , ...

Q2   Choose from the words below to fill in the spaces in the passage.

high   low   vibrate

A sound wave makes air molecules .... If there are

many vibrations per second the frequency or pitch of the sound is

.... If there are only a few vibrations per second the pitch

of the sound is ....

Q3   Complete the sentences below by circling the correct word in each pair.

The bigger the **amplitude / frequency** of a sound wave, the **louder / quieter** the sound.

Q4   A bell is vibrating with a frequency of 2 kHz. How many times a second is it vibrating?

....

Q5   Most humans can hear sounds in the frequency range 20 Hz to 20 000 Hz.

a)   What is the frequency of a sound wave that has 30 compressions in one second?

....

b)   Put the following frequencies in order, from the lowest frequency to the highest.

3 MHz, 8 kHz, 630 Hz, 400 kHz, 5 Hz, 21 kHz

....

Sound Waves

Q6   Mina sings in her school choir. She practises both in her bedroom
and in an empty practice room at school. She hears a difference in
the sound of her voice, caused by a difference in echo.

a)   What is an echo?

....

....

b)   Why were there lots of echoes in the unfurnished practice room but not in her bedroom at home?

....

....

c)   Why is there a delay before you hear an echo?

....

....

Q7   In an experiment, a ringing alarm clock is placed in a glass bell jar.
Air is sucked out of the jar by a vacuum pump.

a)   What happens to the sound and why?

....

....

b)   Why does the experiment work better if the alarm clock is placed on top of a block of foam?

....

....

Top Tips: I know what you're thinking — it's an outrage what these alarm clocks have to go
through in the name of science. Why not calm yourself though, by making sure you know all the stuff
about sound off the last two pages, like what an echo is and how pitch is determined by frequency.

The Origin of the Universe

Q1   Francesca is standing by a busy street when an ambulance rushes past, with its sirens blaring.

a)   As the ambulance moves away, how will the siren sound different to Francesca?
Underline the correct answer.

It will sound higher pitched   **It will sound lower pitched**

b)   What is the name of this effect?

....

c)   As the ambulance moves away, what happens to the
wavelength of the sound waves heard by Francesca?

....

d)   How would the frequency of the sound wave Francesca heard
have changed as the ambulance approached her?

....

Q2   Brian set up a microphone at his local railway station to record his favourite **train noises**.
He attached the microphone to an oscilloscope.

An express train passed through the station at a constant speed. Diagram A below shows the trace
on the monitor at 11:31:07, as the train **approached** Brian's microphone.

On diagram B, sketch
the trace Brian might have
seen as the train **left** the
station.

A

B

11:31:07

11:31:08

Q3   What **evidence** is there to support the idea that the universe is **expanding**?
Include a brief explanation of **red-shift** in your answer.

....

....

....

....

The Origin of the Universe

Q4 Many cosmologists believe that the universe began with a Big Bang.

a) Briefly describe the Big Bang theory.

....

....

....

....

b) According to the Big Bang theory, what is happening to space itself?

....

Q5 The Big Bang theory is currently the only theory that can explain the existence of cosmic microwave background radiation (CMBR).

a) What is cosmic microwave background radiation?

....

....

b) How does the Big Bang theory explain CMBR?

....

....

....

Q6 The Big Bang theory can't explain everything about the universe. Describe **one** limitation of the Big Bang theory.

....

....

....

Top Tips: Crikey, the question of how the universe started is a pretty big question. Make sure you know all about the Big Bang theory and the evidence that supports it. It's interesting stuff, I reckon.

Mixed Questions — Physics 1b

Q1 The waves A, B and C represent **infrared**, **visible light** and **ultraviolet** radiation (not in that order).

a) Tick the box next to any of the following statements which are true.

☐ B represents ultraviolet radiation.

☐ The infrared wave has the largest amplitude.

☐ C has the highest frequency.

☐ A has the shortest wavelength.

b) Which of the following things do the three waves have in common? Circle the letter(s) of the correct answer(s).

A — They have the same frequency.

B — They are all transverse waves.

C — They transfer the same amount of energy.

D — They travel at the same speed in space.

Q2 A group of farmers live on a remote island, growing potatoes and farming llamas. They decide to put **solar cells** on the roofs of their houses and put up **wind turbines** in their fields.

a) Suggest why the farmers have chosen to use:

i) solar power ....

....

....

ii) wind power ....

....

....

b) What other renewable sources of energy could the farmers use?

....

Mixed Questions — Physics 1b

Q3   Radio Roary transmits **radio** signals with a wavelength of **1.5 km**.

a)   Calculate the **frequency** of Radio Roary's transmission. (Use speed = 3×10^8 m/s.)

....

....

b)   Mr Potts is on holiday in the Scottish Highlands. He follows England's
progress in the cricket test match on Radio Roary, but he can't watch
the coverage on television, because TV reception at the cottage is so poor.

Explain why Mr Potts gets **good** long-wave radio reception,
but such **poor** TV reception.

....

....

Q4   A council are discussing plans to build a new power station.

a)   Give one advantage of nuclear power.

....

b)   Some council members are concerned about the effect fossil-fuel power stations have on the
environment. How does carbon capture and storage technology help reduce these effects?

....

....

Q5   Infrared radiation is used by TV **remote controls**. Jake shows Peter that he can change
the TV channel by pointing the remote control at a mirror on the opposite wall.

a)   What property of EM rays has Jake demonstrated? Circle the correct answer.

reflection   refraction   diffraction

b)   Draw a ray diagram below to show the path of the
radiation emitted from the remote control to the TV.

TV remote sensor   mirror

TV remote

Physics 1b — Electricity and Waves

Mixed Questions — Physics 1b

Q6   A coal-fired power station generates electricity throughout the
day and night, even though there is less demand for electricity overnight.

a)   Describe one way 'spare' night-time electricity can be used to store energy for later use.

....

....

....

b)   List three things that could help the National Grid match supply with demand.

1. ....

2. ....

3. ....

Q7   Mobile phones use microwaves. These waves can spread out
as they pass through a gap, or move past an object.

a)   What is the **technical name** for this spreading out?

....

b)   How does the **size** of the gap affect the **amount** that it spreads out?

....

c)   Describe the **possible health risks** associated with using mobile phones.

....

....

Q8   A pebble is dropped into still water. Waves move out across
the surface of the water. The wavelength is **2 cm** and the waves
are generated at a rate of **10 per second**.

a)   What is the **wavelength** in metres?

....

b)   What is the **frequency** of the wave in Hz?

....

c)   What is the **speed** of the wave?

....

Mixed Questions — Physics 1b

Q9 Electricity is generated in **power stations** and reaches our homes by a network of **power cables**.

a) Describe how electricity is produced in a gas-fired power station.

....

....

....

....

b) Natural gas is a fossil fuel. Burning it releases carbon dioxide and contributes to climate change.

i) Suggest two alternative types of fuel which could be used to produce heat in power stations without contributing to climate change.

.... and ....

ii) It is now possible to install solar cells and wind turbines on the roof of a house. Explain why few households in the UK could rely on these technologies for their electricity supply.

....

....

c) i) Explain why electricity transmission cables are at very high voltages.

....

....

ii) Explain why the high voltage of the cables is not dangerous for people using the electricity.

....

....

Q10 The diagram represents a **light wave** emitted from Cygnus A — a galaxy about 700 million light years from Earth.

a) On the diagram, redraw the wave to show how it might appear to us on Earth because the light is **red-shifted**.

b) Explain how red-shifts from distant and nearer galaxies provide evidence for the Big Bang theory.

....

....

....

Velocity and Distance-Time Graphs

Q1   The **monorail** at Buffers' Theme Park takes people from the visitor centre to the main park and back again. It travels at the same **speed** on the outward and return journeys.

The monorail's velocity on the outward journey is 12 m/s. What is its velocity on the return journey?

....

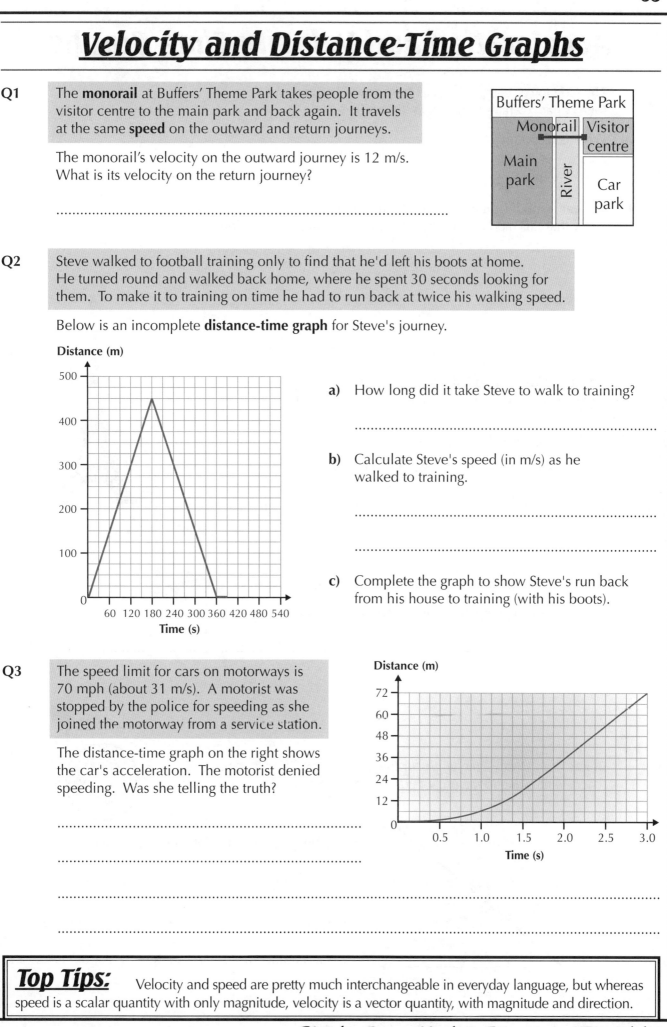

Buffers' Theme Park
Monorail | Visitor centre
Main park
River
Car park

Q2   Steve walked to football training only to find that he'd left his boots at home. He turned round and walked back home, where he spent 30 seconds looking for them. To make it to training on time he had to run back at twice his walking speed.

Below is an incomplete **distance-time graph** for Steve's journey.

Distance (m)

a)   How long did it take Steve to walk to training?

....

b)   Calculate Steve's speed (in m/s) as he walked to training.

....

....

c)   Complete the graph to show Steve's run back from his house to training (with his boots).

Q3   The speed limit for cars on motorways is 70 mph (about 31 m/s). A motorist was stopped by the police for speeding as she joined the motorway from a service station.

The distance-time graph on the right shows the car's acceleration. The motorist denied speeding. Was she telling the truth?

....

....

Distance (m)

....

....

Top Tips: Velocity and speed are pretty much interchangeable in everyday language, but whereas speed is a scalar quantity with only magnitude, velocity is a vector quantity, with magnitude and direction.

<u>Acceleration and Velocity-Time Graphs</u>

Q1   The Go Go car company make gas-powered model cars.
One car accelerates from rest to 20 m/s in 3.5 s.

   a)   What is its acceleration?

   ....

   b)   The car is modified and now accelerates from 3 m/s to 20 m/s in 2.8 s.
Show that this modification has improved the car's acceleration.

   ....

   ....

Q2   An egg is dropped from the top of the Eiffel tower.
It hits the ground after 8 seconds, at a speed of 80 m/s.

   a)   Find the egg's acceleration.   ....

   b)   How long did it take for the egg to reach 40 m/s?

   ....

Q3   A car accelerates at 2 m/s². After 4 seconds it reaches a speed of 24 m/s.

   How fast was it going before it started to accelerate?

   ....

   ....

Q4   Below is a velocity-time graph for the descent of a lunar lander.
It accelerates due to the pull of gravity from the Moon.

Use the graph to calculate this acceleration.

   ....

   ....

   ....

Acceleration and Velocity-Time Graphs

Q5   Describe the **type of motion** happening at each of the labelled points on the velocity-time graph.

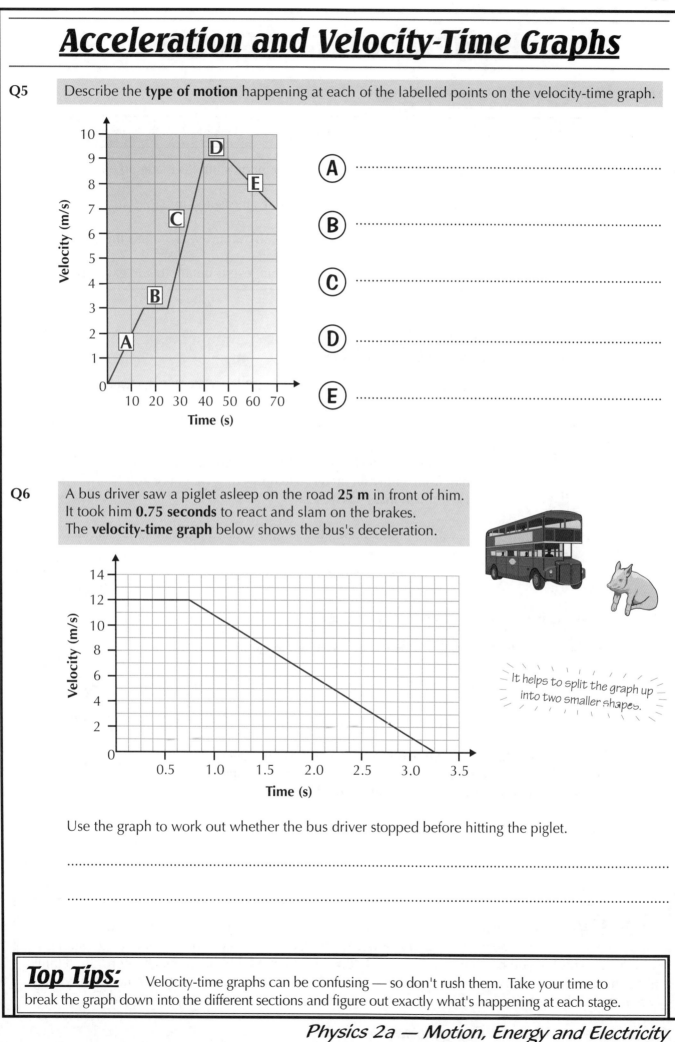

(A) ....

(B) ....

(C) ....

(D) ....

(E) ....

Q6   A bus driver saw a piglet asleep on the road **25 m** in front of him.
It took him **0.75 seconds** to react and slam on the brakes.
The **velocity-time graph** below shows the bus's deceleration.

It helps to split the graph up into two smaller shapes.

Use the graph to work out whether the bus driver stopped before hitting the piglet.

....

....

Top Tips: Velocity-time graphs can be confusing — so don't rush them. Take your time to break the graph down into the different sections and figure out exactly what's happening at each stage.

Weight, Mass and Gravity

Q1   Fill in the gaps in the following paragraph using the words below:

kilograms	newtons	mass	weight	gravitational

The .... of an object is just the amount of 'stuff' it's made up of. It doesn't

change, regardless of where in the universe it is, and it's measured in ....

.... is a force and is measured in .... — it's the

.... force that one object (e.g. a planet) exerts on another (e.g. an apple).

Q2   Joni has been feeding her dog Fluffy a bit too much bacon. The vet decides he needs to go on a diet.

g = 10 N/kg

a)   Joni puts Fluffy on some scales and finds he has a mass of **58 kg**. Calculate his **weight**.

....

b)   After three weeks of Fluffy eating only 'Skinny Dog' biscuits, Joni weighs Fluffy by putting him in a sling and hanging him from a **newton meter**. He now has a weight of **460 N**. How much **mass** has he lost?

....

....

Q3   An astronaut goes to Mars to do some experiments.

a)   Explain why her **mass** stays the same but her **weight** changes.

Woohoo!
Who needs diets?
Just go to Mars...

....

....

b)   She takes a rock that weighs **50 N** on Earth. Using a set of scales designed for use on Earth, she finds that the mass of the rock appears to be **1.9 kg** on Mars. Calculate the **gravitational field strength** on Mars.

....

....

> ## Top Tips: Gravity may be keeping you down to the earth, but compared to the other
> fundamental forces, it is actually **surprisingly weak**. Think about it — you have whole Earth pulling
> you downwards but you can jump and hop and skip away from it without too much effort. Then think
> about how much effort it can take to pull opposite ends of a small magnet apart. The fact is, **anything
> that has mass has gravity**, but objects have to be pretty humongous before anyone notices.

Resultant Forces

Q1   A teapot sits on a table.

a)   Explain why it doesn't sink into the table.

....

b)   Chris carelessly knocks the teapot off the table and it accelerates towards the floor.

    i)   Explain whether the vertical forces are balanced.

....

    ii)   The teapot hits the floor without breaking and bounces upwards.
      Name the force that causes the teapot to bounce upwards.

....

Q2   A bear rides a bike north at a constant speed.

a)   Label the forces acting on the bear.

b)   The bear brakes and slows down.
Are the forces balanced **as** he
slows down? If not, which
direction is the resultant force in?

....

Q3   The **force diagram** on the right shows a **train** pulling out of a station.

Calculate the resultant force acting on
the train in the following directions:

1 500 000 N

6 000 000 N

1 500 000 N

1 500 000 N

a)   Vertical: ....

b)   Horizontal: ....

Q4   State whether there is a resultant force in each of the following situations. Explain your answers.

a)   A cricket ball slowing down as it rolls along the outfield.

....

b)   A car going round a roundabout at a steady 30 mph.

....

c)   A vase sat on a window ledge.

....

Forces and Acceleration

Q1   Use the words supplied to fill in the blanks in the paragraph below.

interact	resultant force	stationary	accelerates
opposite	constant	non-zero	balanced

If the forces on an object are ……………...…......... , it's either ……………...…........

or moving at ……………...…......... speed. If an object has a ……………...…........

resultant force acting on it, it ……………...…......... in the direction of the

……………...…......... . When two objects ……………...…......... ,

the forces they exert on each other are equal and ……………...…......... .

Q2   You're travelling home from school on a bus doing a steady speed in a straight line.
Which of the following is true? Tick the appropriate box.

☐   The driving force of the engine is bigger than friction and air resistance combined.

☐   There are no forces acting on the bus.

☐   The driving force of the engine is equal to friction and air resistance combined.

☐   A resultant force is required to keep the bus moving.

Q3   The diagram below shows the **forces** acting on an aeroplane.

a)   The aircraft is flying horizontally at a constant speed of 200 m/s. Which of the following
statements about the aeroplane is true? Circle the appropriate letter.

A   The thrust is bigger than the air resistance and the lift is bigger than the weight.

B   The thrust is smaller than the air resistance and the lift is equal to the weight.

C   The thrust is equal to the air resistance and the lift is equal to the weight.

D   The thrust is equal to the air resistance and the lift is bigger than the weight.

b)   What happens to the forces as the plane descends for landing and slows down to 100 m/s?
Choose the correct options to complete the following statements:

i) The thrust is **greater than / less than / equal to** the air resistance.

ii) The lift is **greater than / less than / equal to** the weight.

*Remember — the plane
is losing height as well
as slowing down.*

Forces and Acceleration

Q4 Put these cars in order of increasing driving force.

Car	Mass (kg)	Maximum acceleration (m/s²)
Disraeli 9000	800	5
Palmerston 6i	1560	0.7
Heath TT	950	3
Asquith 380	790	2

1..

2..

3..

4..

Q5 Jo and Brian have fitted both their scooters with the same engine. Brian and his scooter have a combined mass of 110 kg and an acceleration of 2.80 m/s². On her scooter, Jo only manages an acceleration of 1.71 m/s².

a) What **force** can the engine exert?

....

b) Calculate the combined mass of Jo and her scooter.

....

Q6 Tom drags a 1 kg mass along a table with a newton-meter so that it accelerates at 0.25 m/s². If the newton-meter reads 0.4 N, what's the force of friction between the mass and the table?

....

....

....

Q7 A car tows a caravan along a road. At a constant speed, the pulling force of the car and the opposing reaction force of the caravan are equal. Which statement correctly describes the forces between the caravan and the car when the car accelerates? Tick the appropriate box.

☐ "The caravan's reaction force cancels out the pulling force of the car, so the caravan won't accelerate."

☐ "The caravan's reaction force is at a right angle to the force pulling the car, so the two forces don't affect one another."

☐ "The car's pulling force accelerates the caravan. The caravan's reaction acts on the car, not the caravan."

Forces and Acceleration

Q8 Which of the following statements correctly explains what happens when you walk?
Tick the appropriate box.

☐ Your feet push backwards on the ground, so the ground pushes you forwards.

☐ The force in your muscles overcomes the friction between your feet and the ground.

☐ The ground's reaction can't push you backwards because of friction.

☐ Your feet push forwards, and the ground's reaction is upwards.

Q9 A camper van with a mass of 2500 kg has a maximum driving force of 2650 N.
It is driven along a straight, level road at a constant speed of 90 kilometres per hour.
At this speed, air resistance is 2000 N and the friction between the wheel bearings is 500 N.

a) i) What force is the engine exerting? ....

ii) Complete the diagram to show all the forces acting on the camper van.
Give the size of each force.

b) A strong headwind begins blowing, with a force of **200 N**. The van slows down.
Calculate its deceleration.

....

c) The driver notices that the van is slowing and puts his foot right down on the accelerator,
applying the maximum driving force. How does the acceleration of the camper van change?
(Assume that air resistance and friction remain at their previous values.)

....

....

....

Top Tips: A resultant force means your object will accelerate — it will change its speed
or direction (or both). But if your object has a constant speed (which could be zero) and a constant
direction, you can say with utter confidence that there ain't any resultant force. Be careful though
— a zero resultant force doesn't mean there are **no** forces, just that they all balance each other out.

Frictional Force and Terminal Velocity

Q1 Use the words supplied to fill in the blanks in the paragraph below about a skydiver. You may need to use some words more than once, or not at all.

decelerates   decrease   less   balances   increase   constant   greater   accelerates

When a skydiver jumps out of a plane, his weight is .... than his air resistance, so he .... downwards. This causes his air resistance to .... until it .... his weight. At this point, his velocity is .... When his parachute opens, his air resistance is .... than his weight, so he ....

This causes his air resistance to .... until it .... his weight. Then his velocity is .... once again.

Q2 Which of the following will **reduce** the air resistance force on an aeroplane? Tick any appropriate boxes.

☐ **flying higher (where the air is thinner)**   ☐ **carrying less cargo**

☐ **flying more slowly**   ☐ **making the plane more streamlined**

Q3 A scientist plans to investigate gravity by dropping a hammer and a feather from a tall building. Two onlookers predict what will happen. Say whether each is right or wrong, and explain why.

Paola: "They will land at the same time — gravity is the same for both."

Guiseppe: "The feather will reach its terminal velocity before the hammer."

a) Paola is **right** / **wrong** because ....

....

b) Guiseppe is **right** / **wrong** because ....

....

Q4 Mavis is investigating **drag** by dropping balls into a measuring cylinder full of oil and timing how long they take to reach the bottom. She does the experiment with a **golf ball**, a **glass marble** and a **ball bearing**.

From this experiment, can Mavis draw any conclusions about the effect of size on drag? Explain your answer.

....

....

Frictional Force and Terminal Velocity

Q5 The graph shows how the velocity of a skydiver changes before and after he opens his parachute.

Velocity

Time

A   B   C   D

For each of the four regions A-D tick the correct box to say whether the force of **weight** or **air resistance** is greater, or if they are **equal**.

	weight is greater	air resistance is greater	both equal
Region A:	☐	☐	☐
Region B:	☐	☐	☐
Region C:	☐	☐	☐
Region D:	☐	☐	☐

Q6 Two skydivers jump out of a plane. Kate opens her parachute after three seconds, when she is still accelerating rapidly. Alison doesn't open her parachute yet but uses her video camera to film Kate's skydive. On the film Kate's parachute appears to pull her suddenly upwards when it opens.

a) Is Kate really moving upwards? Explain your answer. ....

....

b) Describe how Kate's velocity changes when her parachute opens. ....

....

Q7 On **Venus**, atmospheric pressure is about 90 times that on Earth, but the gravitational field strength is about the same.
On **Mars**, atmospheric pressure is about 1/100th of that on Earth and the gravitational field strength is less than half that on Earth.

Higher atmospheric pressure means the atmosphere is <u>thicker</u> and provides <u>more resistance</u>.

Probes which land on other planets often need parachutes to slow them down during their descent. What **size** of parachute would you recommend, relative to a parachute used on Earth, for:

a) landing on Venus: ....

b) landing on Mars: ....

Top Tips: When objects move through the air at high speed, the air resistance is proportional to the object's **velocity squared**. That's why, for skydivers, air resistance soon balances their weight and they reach terminal velocity. It's also why **driving** very fast is very **inefficient**.

Stopping Distances

Q1   **Stopping distance** and **braking distance** are not the same thing.

    a)   What is meant by 'braking distance'?

        ....

    b)   What is meant by 'thinking distance'?

        ....

Q2   Will the following factors affect **thinking** distance, **braking** distance or **both**?
Write them in the relevant columns of the table.

tiredness   road surface   weather   speed   drugs
    alcohol   tyres   brakes   load

Thinking Distance	Braking Distance

Q3   A car joins a motorway and changes speed from 30 mph to 60 mph.
Which of the following statements are **true**? Tick the appropriate boxes.

☐   The total stopping distance will increase.

☐   The braking force needed to stop in a certain distance will decrease.

☐   Thinking distance will decrease.

☐   Both thinking and braking distance will increase.

Q4   A car has just driven through a deep puddle, making the brakes wet.
Explain why this will increase the stopping distance of the car.

    ....

    ....

Q5   Sam is driving when she receives a text message. She decides to try and read it
while still driving. Does this affect her thinking distance? Explain your answer.

    ....

    ....

Work and Potential Energy

Q1   Jenny kicks a football, giving it **50 J** of energy.

a)   How much work does Jenny do?

....

b)   If Jenny kicks the ball with a force of **250 N**, over what **distance** does her kick act on the ball?

....

Q2   Explain why pushing your bicycle along a **level** road means that you do some **work** in the scientific sense.

....

....

Q3   Indicate whether the following statements are **true** or **false**.

		True	False
a)	Gravitational potential energy = mass × g × height.	☺	☹
b)	Work done is the energy possessed by an object due to height.	☺	☹
c)	On Earth, the gravitational field strength is approximately **10 N/kg**.	☺	☹
d)	When a force moves an object, work is done.	☺	☹
e)	On Earth, a **3 kg** chicken flies up 2.5 m to sit on a fence. It gains **90 J** of gravitational potential energy.	☺	☹

Q4   Dave works at a DIY shop. He has to load **28** flagstones onto the delivery truck. Each flagstone has a mass of **25 kg** and has to be lifted **1.2 m** onto the truck.

a)   How much gravitational potential energy does one flagstone gain when lifted onto the truck?

....

b)   What is the **total gravitational potential energy** gained by the flagstones after they are all loaded onto the truck?

....

c)   How much **work** does Dave do loading the truck?

....

....

Top Tips: The main thing to remember is that **energy transferred** and **work done** are just the **same** thing. You're bound to get asked to do a calculation, so make sure you know the couple of equations and how to use them. All work questions are pretty similar — so just keep practising and you'll be fine.

Work and Potential Energy

Q5 Shelagh keeps fit by cycling every day. She's calculated that she applies a **steady force** of **50 N** as she cycles. She decides to do at least **80 kJ** of work at each session.

a) What is the minimum distance Shelagh needs to cycle each session?

....

b) i) Shelagh unexpectedly comes to a large hill. She does **90 kJ** of work to climb a vertical height of **120 m**. Calculate the size of the force she does work against. Name this force.

....

....

ii) Calculate the combined mass of Shelagh and her bike.

....

Q6 Jo is sitting at the top of a helter-skelter ride and her mass is **50 kg**.

a) If her gravitational potential energy is **4000 J**, how high up is Jo?

....

b) She comes down the helter-skelter and at the bottom her kinetic energy is **1500 J**. How much **energy** has been 'wasted' coming down the ride?

....

c) Which **force** causes this energy to be wasted? ....

d) If the ride is **50 m** long, what is the average energy-wasting force?

....

e) Jo has another go on the helter-skelter but this time she slides down on a mat. At the bottom of the ride, her kinetic energy is **2000 J**. What is the average energy-wasting **force** on this turn on the ride?

....

....

f) Explain why Jo has a **different** kinetic energy at the bottom when she slides down on a mat.

....

g) At the bottom of the ride Jo and the mat take a distance of **5 m** to stop. What is the average stopping **force**?

....

5 m

....

Kinetic Energy

Q1   Decide if the following statements are **true** or **false**.

		True	False
a)	Kinetic energy is energy due to movement.	☺	☹
b)	Heat from the Sun causes space shuttles to heat up as they re-enter the atmosphere.	☺	☹
c)	Friction between meteors and the atmosphere causes most meteors to burn up before they reach the Earth.	☺	☹

Q2   A toy cricket ball hit straight upwards has a gravitational potential energy of **242 J** at the **top** of its flight.

a)   What is the ball's **kinetic energy just** before it hits the ground?

....

b)   Calculate the speed of the ball at this time if its mass is **100 g**.

....

Q3   A large truck and a car both have a kinetic energy of **614 400 J**. The mass of the truck is **12 288 kg** and the car **1200 kg**.

a)   Calculate the **speed** of:

i) the car ....

ii) the truck ....

b)   John is playing with his remote-controlled toy car and truck. The car's mass is 100 g. The truck's mass is 300 g. The car is moving twice as fast as the truck. Which has more kinetic energy — the car or the truck? Explain your answer.

....

....

Q4   Jack rides his bicycle along a level road and has a total kinetic energy of **1440 J**. He brakes, exerting a force of **200 N** on the wheels.

a)   How far does he travel before he stops?

....

b)   What happens to the temperature of the brakes? Explain your answer.

....

> **Top Tips:**   It's all about moving — the bigger the mass and the faster something moves the larger its kinetic energy. Get friendly with that formula — it crops up everywhere.

Physics 2a — Motion, Energy and Electricity

Forces and Elasticity

Q1   Alice is bouncing on a trampoline. Springs around the edge hold the trampoline bed in place.

a)   The springs that hold the trampoline bed are **elastic objects**. Describe what 'elastic' means.

....

b)   When she is at the top of a bounce
Alice has **gravitational potential energy**.
This is transferred to **kinetic energy** as
she falls back down, but at the bottom
of the bounce the kinetic energy is **zero**.
Explain what happens to her kinetic energy.

....

....

c)   Alice exerts a force of 600 N on the trampoline at the bottom of her bounce

i)   There are 30 springs that support the trampoline bed. Calculate the **force exerted per spring**.
Assume that **only the springs extend**, and that this force is **evenly spread** across the springs.

....

ii)   An individual spring extends by **10 cm** at the bottom of a bounce. Calculate its **spring constant**.

....

....

Q2   Nick the bungee jumper is checking his bungee cords.

a)   One cord has a spring constant **45 N/m**. Calculate how much force is required to stretch it by **15 m**.

....

b)   Nick conducts an experiment to find how much force it takes to stretch the bungee rope by
different amounts. His results are plotted on the graph below and a best fit line is drawn.

i)   Name the point labelled **P**.

....

ii)   Explain why the shape of the graph changes after point **P**.

....

....

....

Power

Q1   Complete this passage by using the words provided.

heat	energy	one hundred	rate	light	watts	joules

> Power is the .... of doing work, or how much .... is
>
> transferred per second. It is measured in .... or ....
>
> per second. A 100 W light bulb transfers .... joules of electrical
>
> energy into .... and .... each second.

Q2   George drives to work every day in a small car with a **power** output of **50 kW**.

a)   Write down an equation that relates **power** to **energy**.

....

b)   If the journey takes **5 minutes**, how much **energy** does the car get from its fuel?

....

c)   One day George's car breaks down and so he cycles to work. The journey takes him
12 minutes and he uses **144 kJ** of energy. How much **power** does he generate?

....

Q3   Catherine and Sally decide to run up a set of stairs to see who can get to the
top more quickly. Catherine has a mass of **46 kg** and Sally has a mass of **48 kg**. $g = 10 \text{ N/kg}$

a)   The top of the stairs is **5 m** above ground.
Calculate the gain in **potential energy** for:

i) Catherine

....

ii) Sally

....

b)   Catherine won the race in **6.2 s**, while Sally took **6.4 s**.
Which girl generated more **power**?

....

....

Power

Q4   Tom likes to build model boats. His favourite boat
is the Carter, which has a motor power of **150 W**.

a)   How much **energy** does the Carter transfer in **10 minutes**?

....

b)   The petrol for the boat's motor can supply **30 kJ/ml**.
What volume of petrol is used up in **10 minutes**?

....

c)   Tom decides to get a model speed boat which transfers **120 kJ** in the same 10 minute journey.
What is the **power** of the engine?

....

Q5   Josie runs home after school so she can watch her favourite TV programme.
She has a mass of **60 kg** and her school bag has a mass of **6 kg**.

a)   At the start of her run, she accelerates steadily from **0** to **8 m/s** in **6 seconds** while carrying her bag.
Calculate her power for this part of her run.

....

b)   Josie gets to her house, she puts **down** her school bag, and then runs up the stairs to her room.
It takes her **4 seconds** to get to the top of the stairs, where she is **5 m** above ground level.
How much power does she generate getting up the stairs?

....

Q6   Andy loves running and wants to improve his starts in sprint races. He uses a timing gate to
measure his maximum speed and how long the start takes him. He has a mass of **70 kg**.

Sprint number	Time taken (s)	Maximum speed (m/s)
1	3.2	8.0
2	3.1	8.2
3	3.3	7.9
4 *	4.6	7.2
5	3.2	7.9

*He slips at the start because his shoes
don't grip properly.

a)   Andy records data for five starts as shown.
Which start data set should be ignored?

....

b)   Calculate the average **time** taken and the
average **speed** achieved in the reliable starts.

....

....

c)   What is Andy's average **power** over the reliable
starts?

....

Momentum and Collisions

Q1   Circle the correct words or phrases to make the following statements true.

a)   If the velocity of a moving object doubles, its **kinetic energy** / **momentum** will double.

b)   If you drop a suitcase out of a moving car, the car's momentum will **decrease** / **increase**.

c)   When two objects collide the total momentum **changes** / **stays the same**.

d)   When a force acts on an object its momentum **changes** / **stays the same**.

Q2   Place the following four trucks in order of increasing momentum.

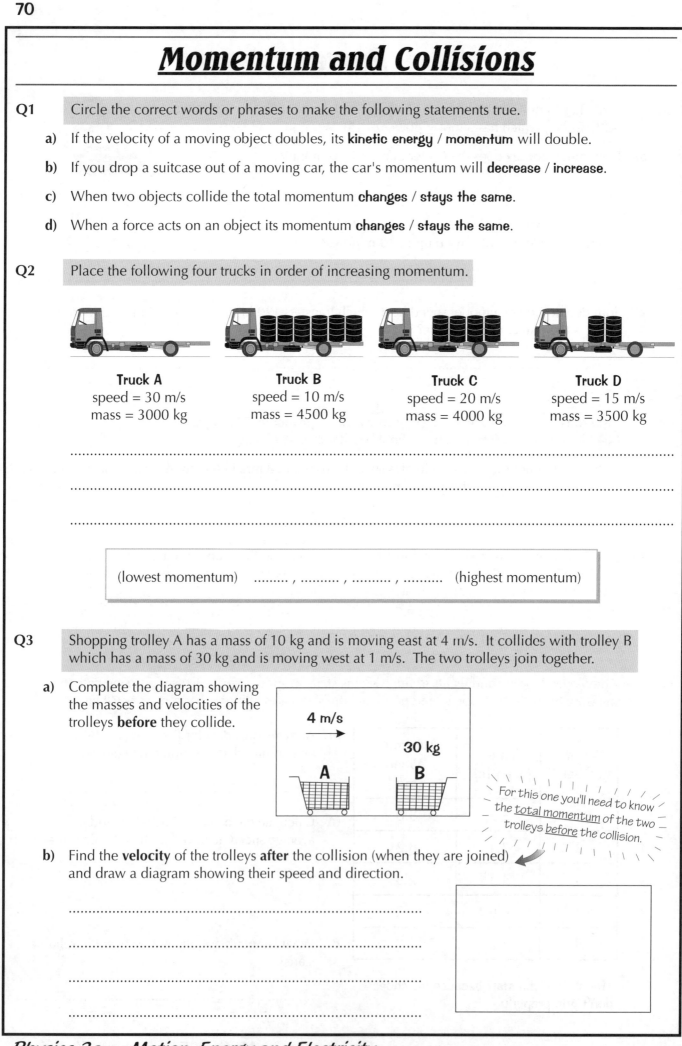

Truck A	**Truck B**	**Truck C**	**Truck D**
speed = 30 m/s	speed = 10 m/s	speed = 20 m/s	speed = 15 m/s
mass = 3000 kg	mass = 4500 kg	mass = 4000 kg	mass = 3500 kg

....

....

....

(lowest momentum)   .... , ... , ... , ...   (highest momentum)

Q3   Shopping trolley A has a mass of 10 kg and is moving east at 4 m/s. It collides with trolley B which has a mass of 30 kg and is moving west at 1 m/s. The two trolleys join together.

a)   Complete the diagram showing the masses and velocities of the trolleys **before** they collide.

4 m/s

30 kg

A   B

For this one you'll need to know the total momentum of the two trolleys before the collision.

b)   Find the **velocity** of the trolleys **after** the collision (when they are joined) and draw a diagram showing their speed and direction.

....

....

....

....

Physics 2a — Motion, Energy and Electricity

Car Design and Safety

Q1   Use the words in the box to fill in the gaps in the paragraph below.

electric generator	reverse	heat	chemical
efficient	work		regenerative

When the brakes of a car are applied, they do .... on the

wheels, transferring kinetic energy into .... and sound

energy. New .... braking systems put the vehicle's motor

into .... to slow the wheels down.

The motor works as an .... and converts the kinetic

energy of the wheels into electrical energy. This can then be used to charge

the vehicle's battery — storing the electrical energy as ....

energy. By finding a use for this previously 'wasted' energy, these new braking

systems make cars more ....

Q2   A car travels along a level road and brakes to avoid hitting a cat.

a)   What type of **energy** does the moving car have?

  ....

b)   Explain how energy is **conserved** as the brakes slow down the car.

  ....

  ....

Q3   Clive's car has a top speed of 150 mph. He attaches a roof box to
his car. How will this affect its top speed? Explain your answer.

  ....

  ....

  ....

Car Design and Safety

Q4   Modern cars are now fitted with many **safety features**, including seat belts.

a)   Explain why car safety features are designed to **slow** the car and
its occupants down over the **longest** possible time in a collision.

....

....

b)   State **two other** safety features which increase the time taken for passengers to slow down in a
crash. For each feature, explain **how** it helps to convert **kinetic energy** more safely.

....

....

....

....

Q5   Since 1991 it has been compulsory in the UK for all adults
to wear seat belts in both the front and back seats of a car.

a)   Explain how a seat belt **absorbs** energy to
slow down a passenger when a crash occurs.

....

b)   Explain, in terms of **momentum changes**, how this protects the passenger's internal organs.

....

....

....

Q6   A sports car transfers **2 650 000 kJ** of chemical energy
per hour into kinetic energy. Calculate its power output.

$power = energy \div time$

....

....

....

Top Tips: In a car crash there's a sudden change in velocity, which means a sudden change in
momentum. To help protect the passengers inside, the car needs to make the momentum change more
slowly — if you're in a serious crash you want the car to be the one all crumpled up, not you.

Physics 2a — Motion, Energy and Electricity

Static Electricity

Q1 **Circle** the pairs of charges that would attract each other and **underline** those that would repel.

positive and positive   positive and negative   negative and positive   negative and negative

Q2 Fill in the gaps in these sentences with the words below.

electrons	positive	static	friction	insulating	negative

.... electricity can build up when two .... materials

are rubbed together. The .... moves .... from one

material onto the other. This leaves a .... charge on one of the

materials and a .... charge on the other.

Q3 The sentences below are wrong. Write out a **correct** version for each.

a) A polythene rod becomes negatively charged when rubbed with a duster because it loses electrons.

....

....

b) When a negatively charged object and a positively charged object are brought together, only the negative object exerts a force.

....

....

c) The closer two charged objects are together, the less strongly they attract or repel.

....

....

d) Electrical charges can't move very easily through metals.

....

....

Q4 Russell hates his jumper. Whenever he takes it off his hair stands on end. Explain why this happens.

....

....

Physics 2a — Motion, Energy and Electricity

Current and Potential Difference

Q1   Use the words below to complete the passage.

reduces	voltage	decrease	charge	work
Electric current is the flow of electric .... around a circuit. Current flows				
through a component which has a potential difference (................................) across it.				
The potential difference between two points in an circuit is the .... done per				
coulomb of charge that passes between the points. Resistance .... the flow				
of current — to increase the current in a circuit you can .... the resistance.				

Q2   Connect the quantities with their units and their symbols.

A   Current   volts

V   Resistance   amps

Ω   Potential Difference   ohms

Q3   A 3 volt battery can supply a current of 5 amps for 20 minutes before it needs recharging.

  a) Calculate how much charge the battery can provide before it needs recharging.

    ....

    Tip: convert to seconds first.

    ....

  b) Each coulomb of charge from the battery can carry 3 J of energy.
         Calculate how much work the battery can do before it needs recharging.

    ....

Q4   Sally is comparing two lamps, A and B. She takes the measurements shown in the table.

Calculate the **missing values** and write them in the table.

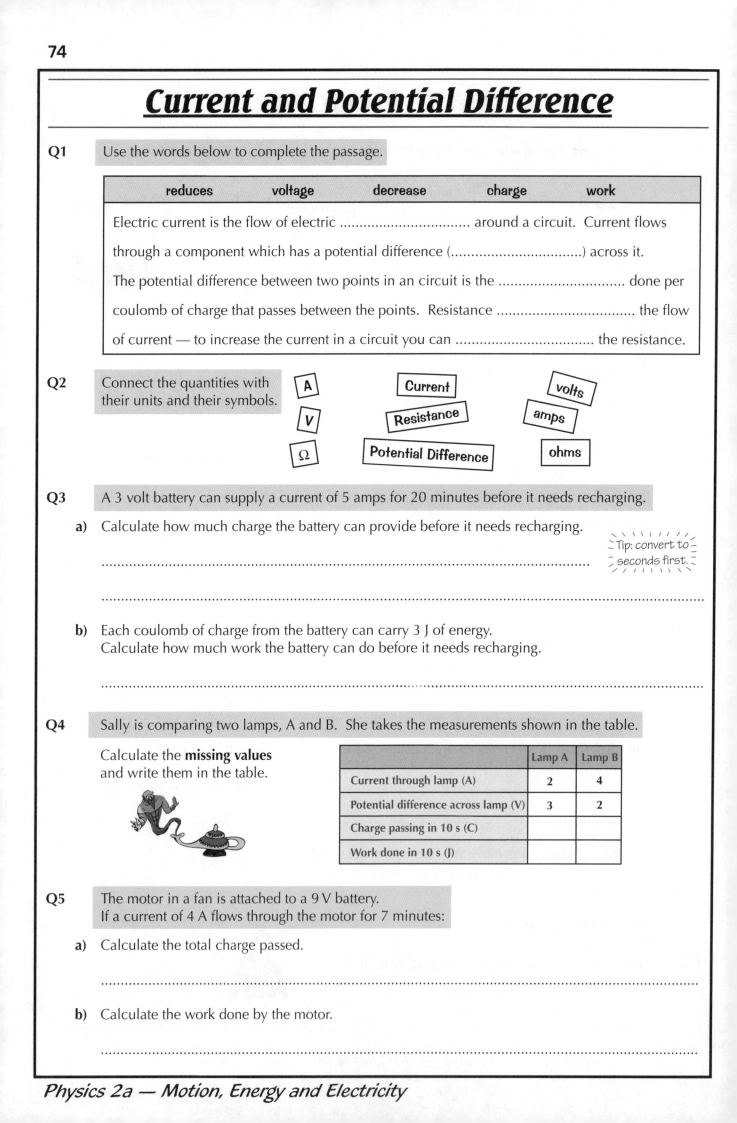

	Lamp A	Lamp B
Current through lamp (A)	2	4
Potential difference across lamp (V)	3	2
Charge passing in 10 s (C)		
Work done in 10 s (J)		

Q5   The motor in a fan is attached to a 9 V battery.
         If a current of 4 A flows through the motor for 7 minutes:

  a) Calculate the total charge passed.

    ....

  b) Calculate the work done by the motor.

    ....

Physics 2a — Motion, Energy and Electricity

Circuits — The Basics

Q1   Match up these items from a standard test circuit with the **correct description** and **symbol**.

ITEM	DESCRIPTION	SYMBOL
Cell	Provides the 'push' on the charge.	
Variable Resistor	The item you're testing.	
Component	Used to alter the current.	
Voltmeter	Measures the current.	
Ammeter	Measures the voltage.	

Q2   Complete the following passage by using the words from the box.

circuit	across	through

You can measure the resistance of a component using a standard test

.... To work out the resistance of the component, you need to

measure the current .... the component using an ammeter

and the potential difference .... it using a voltmeter.

Q3   The diagram below shows a **complete circuit**.

Wilkins, drop and give me ten circuits, complete with ammeter and voltmeter.

Mr Smith was keen on circuit training.

a)   Give the name of each of the numbered components.

1. ....   2. ....

3. ....   4. ....

5. ....   6. ....

b)   Draw an **ammeter** on the circuit in the correct position to measure the current leaving the battery.

c)   Draw a **voltmeter** on the circuit in the correct position to measure the voltage across the lamp.

Resistance and V = I × R

Q1   Match the correct label to each of the **V-I graphs** below.

RESISTOR   FILAMENT LAMP   DIODE

A ....   B ....   C ....

Q2   Indicate whether the following are **true** or **false**.

		True	False
a)	The resistance of a filament lamp falls as the temperature of the filament increases.	☐	☐
b)	The steeper the gradient of a V-I graph, the lower the resistance.	☐	☐
c)	Current can flow freely through a diode in both directions.	☐	☐
d)	The current through a resistor at constant temperature is proportional to the voltage.	☐	☐
e)	Current can flow both ways through a lamp.	☐	☐

Q3   The graph below shows V-I curves for four resistors.

Gradient = $\dfrac{\text{vertical change}}{\text{horizontal change}}$

a)   Which resistor has the highest resistance? ....

b)   Calculate the gradient of the line for resistor B.

   ....

c)   Calculate the resistance of resistor B.

   ....

Q4   An electrical current flowing through a **filament bulb** causes it to get **hot**. Explain why this makes its resistance **increase**. You should give your answer in terms of **electrons** and **ions**.

   ....

   ....

   ....

   ....

Physics 2a — Motion, Energy and Electricity

Resistance and $V = I \times R$

Q5　Fill in the missing values in the table below.

Use the formula triangle to help.

Voltage (V)	Current (A)	Resistance (Ω)
6	2	
8		2
	3	3
4	8	
2		4
	0.5	2

Q6　Peter tested **three components** using a standard test circuit. The table below shows his results.

Voltage (V)	−4.0	−3.0	−2.0	−1.0	0.0	1.0	2.0	3.0	4.0
Component **A** current (A)	−2.0	−1.5	−1.0	−0.5	0.0	0.5	1.0	1.5	2.0
Component **B** current (A)	0.0	0.0	0.0	0.0	0.0	0.2	1.0	2.0	4.5
Component **C** current (A)	−4.0	−3.5	−3.0	−2.0	0.0	2.0	3.0	3.5	4.0

a)　Draw a **V-I graph** for each component on the axes below.

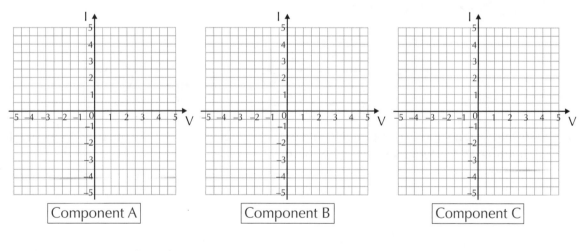

Component A　　　　Component B　　　　Component C

b)　Complete Peter's **conclusions**:

Component **A** is a ....

Component **B** is a ....

Component **C** is a ....

Top Tips:　There are two very important skills you need to master for resistance questions — **interpreting V-I graphs** and using the formula **V = I × R**. Make sure you can do both.

Circuit Devices

Q1   Use the words below to fill in the gaps. You won't need to use all the words.

light-dependent	lights	thermistor	vary	thermostats	diode

The resistance of some components can .... The resistance of a

.... goes up as the temperature decreases — this makes them useful as

electronic .... The resistance of a .... resistor

depends on the intensity of light falling on it — its resistance drops when light shines on it.

They're often used to automatically switch on .... when it gets dark.

Q2   **LEDs** are used in electrical appliances and for lighting.

a)   Briefly describe how an LED works.

....

b)   Suggest **one** reason why there is an increasing use of LEDs as lighting.

....

....

Q3   Look at the components below.

a)   Use **some** of the above components to design a circuit that will vary the brightness of a **lamp**, depending on the **temperature** in the room.

b)   What happens to the **resistance** in the circuit as the room temperature **increases**?

....

c)   What happens to the **brightness** of the lamp as the room temperature **decreases**?

....

Series Circuits

Q1   Match up these definitions with what they describe in a series circuit.

Same everywhere in the circuit

Shared by all the components

The sum of the resistances

Can be different for each component

Potential difference

Current

Total potential difference

Total resistance

Q2   Eva has drawn a series circuit she plans to set up, but she's made **three** mistakes.

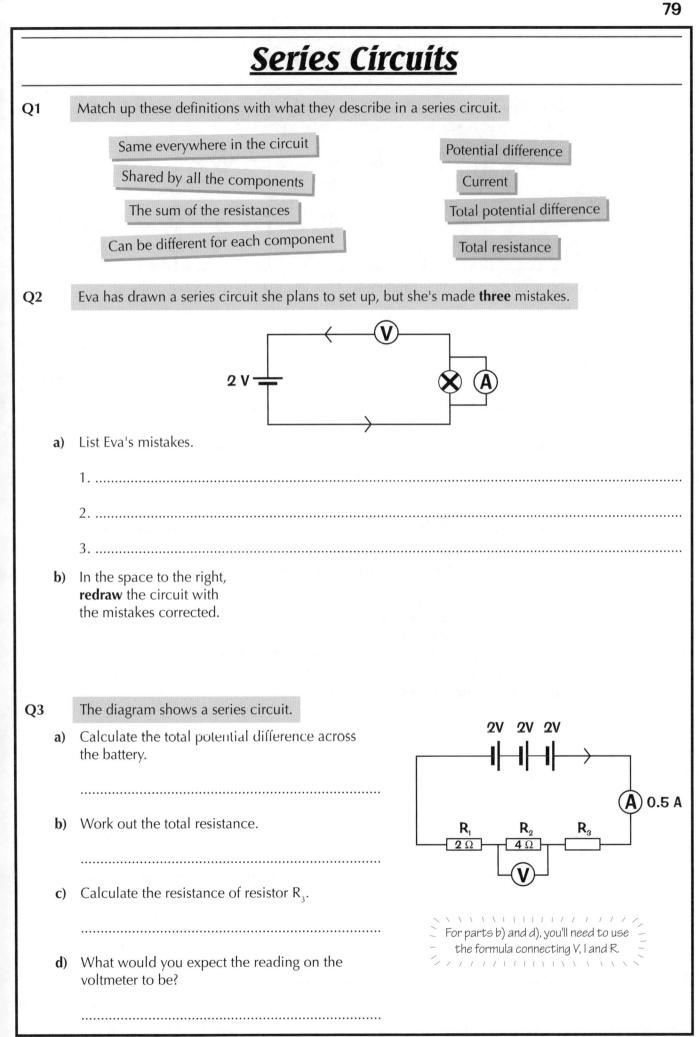

a) List Eva's mistakes.

1. ....

2. ....

3. ....

b) In the space to the right,
redraw the circuit with
the mistakes corrected.

Q3   The diagram shows a series circuit.

a) Calculate the total potential difference across
the battery.

....

b) Work out the total resistance.

....

c) Calculate the resistance of resistor R_3.

....

d) What would you expect the reading on the
voltmeter to be?

....

For parts b) and d), you'll need to use
the formula connecting V, I and R.

Physics 2a — Motion, Energy and Electricity

Series Circuits

Q4   Vikram does an experiment with different numbers of lamps in a series circuit. The diagram below shows his three circuits.

a)   What do you think happens to the **brightness** of the lamps as he adds more of them? **Explain** your answer.

....

....

b)   How does the **current** change as more lamps are added? **Explain** your answer.

....

....

Q5   Here are some instructions for making a series circuit that will **vary the speed of a motor**:

> Connect the following in series...
>
> Two batteries — 3 V each
> Variable resistor
> Ammeter
> Motor of resistance 2 Ω (symbol Ⓜ)

a)   Use the instructions to **draw** the circuit.

b)   What happens to the **speed** of the motor as the resistance of the variable resistor is increased?

....

c)   Calculate the **current** in the circuit when the resistance of the variable resistor is **1 Ω**.

....

....

Parallel Circuits

Q1 Tick to show whether these statements about parallel circuits are **true** or **false**.

		True	False
a)	Components are connected side-by-side (instead of end-to-end).	☐	☐
b)	Each component has the same potential difference across it.	☐	☐
c)	The current is the same everywhere in the circuit.	☐	☐
d)	Components can be switched on and off independently.	☐	☐

Q2 The diagrams show currents at junctions in two parallel circuits.

Write in the **missing** values.

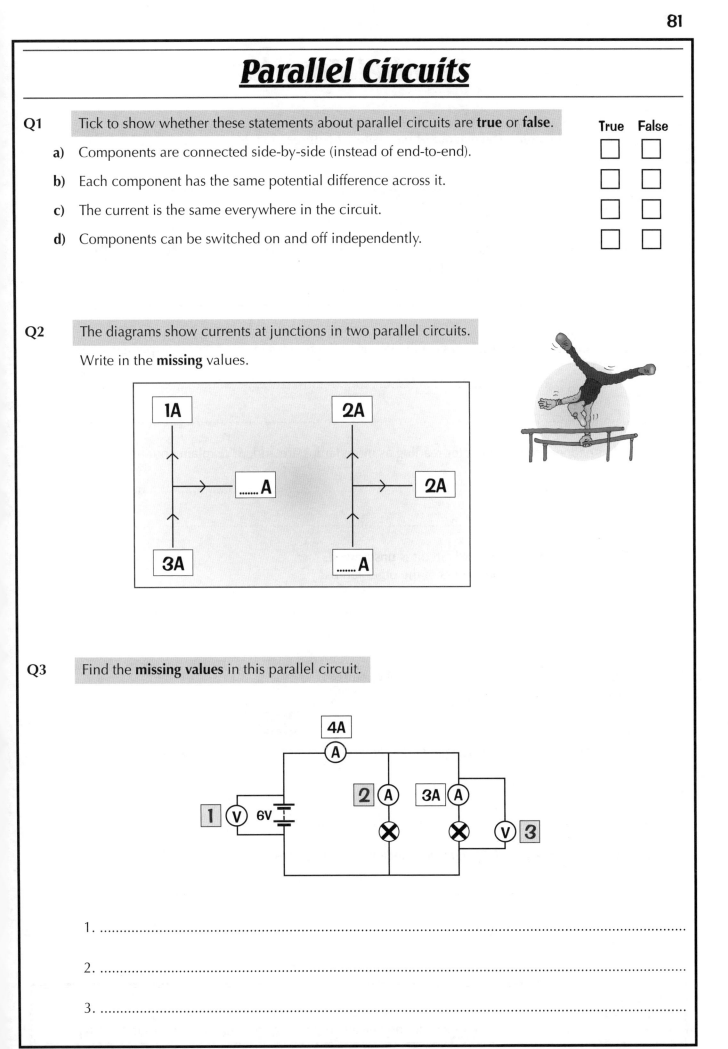

Q3 Find the **missing values** in this parallel circuit.

1. ....

2. ....

3. ....

Parallel Circuits

Q4 Karen does an experiment with different numbers of lamps in a parallel circuit. The diagrams below show her three circuits.

a) What happens to the **brightness** of the lamps as Karen adds more of them? **Explain** your answer.

....

....

b) What happens to the **ammeter** reading as more lamps are added? **Explain** your answer.

....

....

c) One of the lamps in the third circuit is **unscrewed**. What happens to the brightness of the other lamps?

....

Q5 Answer Shane's questions about parallel circuits. Make sure you explain your answers.

a) *"Can you have a different voltage and a different current in each branch of the circuit?"*

....

....

b) *"Why do we use parallel circuits for the lights in our homes?"*

....

....

Top Tips: It's really important you know the differences between series and parallel circuits. Make sure you understand what happens to the current and voltage across components in both types.

Series and Parallel Circuits — Examples

Q1   **Complete** this table for series and parallel circuits:

	SERIES CIRCUITS	PARALLEL CIRCUITS
Components connected	end to end	
Current		can be different in each branch
Voltage	shared between components	
Example of use		

Q2   A set of **Christmas tree lights** is designed to work on mains voltage (230 V). It has **12 V** bulbs.

a)   How can you tell that these lights are wired in series?

....

....

b)   Why might it be better to wire Christmas tree lights in **parallel**?

....

....

c)   Give one reason why you can't usually swap bulbs between series and parallel sets of lights.

....

....

Q3   Fill in the **four** missing values on this **series** circuit:

V_0 = ...

12V

A_2 = 1A (A)

(A) A_1 = ...

2Ω   4Ω

V_3 = ...

V_2 = 2V

V_1 = ...

Series and Parallel Circuits — Examples

Q4 The diagram opposite shows a **parallel** circuit.

a) Calculate the readings on ammeters:

   i) A_1 ....

   ii) A_2 ....

b) Find the readings on voltmeters:

   i) V_1 ....

   ii) V_2 ....

c) What is the reading on ammeter A_0 when switch A is open?

   ....

   ....

Q5 A group of pupils make the following **observations**:

   1. "The lights go dim if you switch the fan on in a parked car."

   2. "You can switch Christmas tree lights off by unscrewing one of the bulbs."

   3. "The lights in my house are wired in parallel, but all the wall lights in the living room go on and off together."

Explain their observations.

1. ....

   ....

   ....

2. ....

   ....

   ....

3. ....

   Think about what makes them go on and off.

   ....

   ....

   ....

Mixed Questions — Physics 2a

Q1 Mr Alonso drives his car at a constant speed for **1500 m**. The engine produces a force of **300 N**.

300 N ➡

a) How much work does the engine do?

....

b) Mr. Alonso then accelerates, increasing his speed by 20 m/s over 6.2 s. Calculate his acceleration.

....

c) As it's a hot day, Mr. Alonso winds down his windows.
Explain how and why this will alter the **top speed** of the car.

....

....

d) Explain how wearing a seat belt will keep Mr. Alonso safer in a crash.

....

Q2 Jack and Jill go up a hill to go on a roller coaster. With them
in it, the roller coaster carriage has a total mass of **1200 kg**.

a) At the start of the ride the carriage rises up to its highest point of **34 m**
above the ground and stops. Calculate its gain in gravitational potential energy.

....

b) The carriage then falls to a third of its maximum height. Assuming there is
no air resistance or friction, calculate the speed of the carriage at this point.

....

....

c) At the end of the ride, the carriage slows down, decelerating at **6.4 m/s²**.
How long does it take the carriage to slow down from 20 m/s and come to a stop?

....

Q3 The diagram shows a circuit in which three resistors are connected in series.

a) Calculate the total resistance of the 3 resistors.

....

10 Ω   5 Ω   5 Ω

b) If the voltmeter shown reads 4 V, find:

i) the current flowing in the circuit. ....

ii) the voltage of the power supply. ....

....

Mixed Questions — Physics 2a

Q4 Norman loves trainspotting. As a special treat, he not only notes the train numbers but plots a **distance-time** graph for two of the trains.

a) For how long is train 2 stationary?

....

b) Calculate the initial speed of the faster train.

....

c) Describe the motion of train 1 between 40 s and 80 s.

....

Q5 Cherie and Tony rob a bank. They escape in a getaway car with a mass of **2100 kg** and travel at a constant speed of **90 km/h** along a straight, level road.

a) Is there a resultant force on the car? Explain your answer.

....

b) Calculate the momentum of the car.

....

c) A police car swings into the middle of the road and stops ahead of Cherie's car. Cherie slams on the brakes. The car comes to a halt **3.0 s** after she hits the brakes.

   i) Write down **one** factor that could affect Cherie's thinking distance.

   ....

   ii) Assuming the car decelerates uniformly, find the force acting on the braking car.

   ....

Q6 The diagram shows a circuit which could be used for the lights on a car.
Each headlight bulb is rated at 12 V, 6 A and each side light bulb is rated at 12 V, 0.5 A.

a) Calculate the total current flowing from the battery if:

   i) Switch A is closed and switch B is open.

   ....

   ii) Switch A is open and switch B is closed. ....

   iii) Switches A and B are both closed. ....

b) The car has a **thermostat** to regulate temperature in the engine. Name the **type** of resistor used in a thermostat and briefly **describe** how this type of resistor works.

....

Mixed Questions — Physics 2a

Q7 In the film 'Crouching Sparrow, Hidden Beaver', a **95 kg** dummy is dropped **60 m** from the top of a building. (Assume that g = 10 m/s².)

a) Sketch a distance-time graph and a velocity-time graph for the dummy from the moment it is dropped until just after it hits the ground.
(Ignore air resistance and assume the dummy does not reach a terminal speed.)

b) The take doesn't go to plan so the dummy is lifted back to the top of the building using a motor.

i) How much work is done on the dummy to get it to the top of the building?

....

ii) The useful power output of the motor is **760 W**.
How long does it take to get the dummy to the top of the building?

....

c) The dummy is getting a bit damaged, being dropped repeatedly, so an elastic cord is attached to it. Calculate the **spring constant** of the cord if it stretches by **5 m** when the dummy is hanging on the end.

....

Q8 A sky-diver jumps out of an aeroplane. Her weight is **700 N**.

a) What force causes her to accelerate downwards?

....

b) After **10 s** she is falling at a steady speed of **60 m/s**.
State the force of air resistance that is acting on her.

....

c) She now opens her parachute, which increases the air resistance to **2000 N**.
Explain what happens immediately after she opens the parachute.

....

....

d) After falling with her parachute open for **5 s**, the sky-diver is travelling at a steady speed of **4 m/s**.
What is the air resistance force now?

....

Mains Electricity

Q1   Choose from the words below to fill in the gaps.

changing	batteries	hertz	d.c.	volts	direct
alternating	a.c.	same	frequency	amps	direction

In the United Kingdom the mains electrical supply is about 230 ....

The supply is .... current (..............) which means that the

.... of the current is constantly ....   The supply

has a .... of 50 cycles per second (50 ....).

Cells and .... supply .... current (................) —

the current always passes in the .... direction.

Q2   The diagram shows three traces on the same CRO. The settings are the same in each case.

A   **B**   **C**

Write down the **letter** of the trace that shows:

a) the highest frequency a.c. ....,   **b)** direct current ....,   **c)** the lowest a.c. voltage ....

Q3   The diagram shows a trace on a CRO screen.
The **timebase** is set to 10 ms per division,
and the **gain** to 1 volt per division.

a)   What is the peak voltage? ....

b)   What is the time period?

....

....

c)   Calculate the frequency of the supply.

....

....

Top Tips: Knowing the difference between a.c. and d.c. isn't too tricky, it's knowing how to work out stuff like the potential difference from a CRO screen that's the hard bit. Learn it all, folks.

Electricity in the Home

Q1   Look at this picture of a kitchen. Put a **ring** round everything that is **unsafe**.

Q2   Answer the following questions about **plugs**:

a)   Why is the body of a plug made of rubber or plastic?

....

b)   Explain why some parts of a plug are made from copper or brass.

....

c)   What material is the cable insulation made from, and why?

....

Q3   Use the words below to complete these rules for wiring a plug.

        outer   bare   live   earth   neutral   insulation   firmly   green and yellow

a)   Strip the .... off the end of each wire.

b)   Connect the brown wire to the .... terminal.

c)   Connect the blue wire to the .... terminal.

d)   Connect the .... wire to the .... terminal.

e)   Check all the wires are .... screwed in with no .... bits showing.

f)   The cable grip must be securely fastened over the .... covering of the cable.

Q4   This plug is **incorrectly** wired. Write down the **three** mistakes.

    1. ....

    2. ....

    3. ....

= Neutral
= Live
= Earth

Fuses and Earthing

Q1   **Match** up the beginnings and endings of these sentences:

The live and neutral wires...	... should be connected to the earth wire.
A circuit breaker...	... should normally carry the same current.
A Residual Current Circuit Breaker...	... does the same job as a fuse.
Any metal casing...	... can be used instead of a fuse and earth wire.
A fuse melts when the current...	... in a fuse wire exceeds the rating of the fuse.

Q2   Put these events in the correct order to describe what happens
when a fault occurs in an earthed kettle. Label the events from 1 to 4.

☐ The device is isolated from the live wire.   ☐ A big current flows out through the earth wire.

☐ A big surge in current blows the fuse.   ☐ A fault allows the live wire to touch the
metal case.

Q3   Some circuits are protected by Residual Current Circuit breakers (RCCBs).

a)   Briefly describe how an RCCB works.

....

....

b)   Give two advantages of using RCCBs instead of fuses.

1. ....

2. ....

Q4   A **'double insulated'** hair dryer uses a current of 0.25 A.

a)   Andrea has fuses rated 0.25 A, 2 A and 8 A.
Which fuse should she fit in the plug for the hair dryer?   ....

b)   Why does the hair dryer **not** need an **earth wire**?

....

c)   What type of electrical cable will the hair dryer have? Circle the correct answer.

two-core cable   three-core cable

d)   Andrea notices the electrical supply cable for her TV is much thicker than for her
hair dryer. Explain how **cable thickness** and **fuse ratings** of appliances are **linked**.

....

....

Energy and Power in Circuits

Q1 Fill in the gaps using the words in the box.

power	energy	more	heat	how long	time

The energy transferred by an appliance depends on .... it's used

for and its .... The power of an appliance can be calculated

using the formula: power = ... ÷ ....

Whenever an electrical current flows through anything with an electrical resistance,

electrical energy is converted into .... energy. The less energy

wasted, e.g. as heat by an appliance, the .... efficient it is.

Q2 Raj is comparing **three** different types of light bulb. Below is a summary of his findings.

	Fluorescent bulb	Light-emitting diode (LED) bulb	Filament bulb
Energy efficiency	~10%	~75%	~2%
Cost	£3.50	£25	50p

a) Suggest **one** reason why the filament bulb has a low efficiency.

....

b) Give **one** reason why Raj might choose to buy the **LED** bulb rather than the other two types.

....

c) Suggest why Raj might choose to buy the filament bulb rather than the other two types.

....

....

Q3 Calculate the **amount** of electrical energy used by the following.
For each component, say what **forms** of energy the electrical energy is converted to.

a) A 100 watt lamp in 10 seconds: .... J.

Electrical energy is converted to .... and .... energy.

b) A 500 watt motor in 2 minutes: .... J.

Electrical energy is converted to ...., ... and .... energy.

c) A 1 kW heater in 20 seconds: .... J.

Electrical energy is converted to .... energy.

d) A 2 kW heater in 10 minutes: .... J.

Electrical energy is converted to .... energy.

Remember to put time in seconds and power in W.

92

Power and Energy Change

Q1 Lucy is comparing **three lamps**. She connects each lamp in a circuit and measures the **current**. Her results are shown in the table below.

	Lamp A	Lamp B	Lamp C
Voltage (V)	12	3	230
Current (A)	2.5	4	0.1
Power (W)			
Energy used in one minute (J)			

a) Complete the table by filling in the missing values.

b) What rating of fuse would each lamp need?

A = ...,   B = ...,   C = ...

Typical fuse ratings are 1, 2, 3, 5, 7, 10 or 13A.

Q2 An electric heater is rated at **230 V**, **1500 W**.

a) Calculate the current it uses.

....

....

b) What rating of fuse should be used with this heater? Circle your choice.

1 A   **2 A**   **3 A**   **5 A**   **7 A**   **10 A**   **13 A**

Q3 Henry is comparing two electric drills. He takes the measurements shown in the table below. Calculate the **missing values** and write them in the table.

	Drill A	Drill B
Current through drill (A)	2	3
Voltage drop across drill (V)	230	230
Charge passing in 5 s (C)		
Energy transformed in 5 s (J)		

Remember, current = charge ÷ time.

Q4 Tim's toy boat has a motor attached to a **2 V** battery. A current of **0.6 A** runs through the boat when it's switched on. Tim turns his boat on and leaves it running in his bath for **12 minutes**.

a) Calculate the total charge passed.

....

b) Calculate the energy transformed by the motor.

....

Physics 2b — Electricity and the Atom

Atomic Structure

Q1 **Complete** the following sentences.

a) Neutral atoms have .... charge.

b) A charged atom is called an ....

c) A neutral atom has the same number of .... and ....

d) If an electron is removed from a neutral atom, the atom becomes .... charged.

Q2 **Complete** this table.

Particle	Mass	Charge
Proton	1	
	1	0
Electron		−1

Q3 In the early 1900s, the '**plum pudding**' model of the atom was replaced by **Rutherford** and **Marsden's** nuclear model.

a) i) Briefly describe the **experiment** Rutherford and Marsden carried out.

....

....

ii) What did they **expect** to happen in the experiment?

....

....

b) Rutherford and Marsden used the results from their experiments to disprove the **plum pudding model** and come up with the **nuclear model** of the atom. Describe the **results** of their experiment, and what they showed about the **structure of the atom**.

....

....

....

....

....

....

Top Tips: Make sure you can explain how the results from Rutherford and Marsden's scattering experiments led to the 'plum pudding' model being replaced by the nuclear model of the atom.

Atoms and Ionising Radiation

Q1 Indicate whether these sentences are **true** or **false**.

		True	False
a)	The total number of neutrons in an atom is called the atomic number.	☐	☐
b)	The total number of protons and neutrons in an atom is called the mass number.	☐	☐
c)	Atoms of the same element with the same number of neutrons are called isotopes.	☐	☐
d)	Radioactive decay speeds up at higher temperatures.	☐	☐
e)	Radioactive decay is a random process — you can't predict when it will happen.	☐	☐

Q2 **Radiation doses** are measured in **Sieverts (Sv)**.

a) While you are reading this you are receiving about 2 mSv/year.

   i) What is causing this?

   ....

   ii) Suggest two **man-made** sources that might contribute to this radiation.

   1. ....

   2. ....

b) The table below shows some typical radiation doses.

	Dose in Sv
50% survival probability, whole body dose	4 (single dose)
Legal worker dose limit (whole body)	0.02 per year
Average dose from all sources in Cornwall	0.008 per year
Average dose from natural radiation	0.002 per year
Average dose from a UK to Spain flight	0.00001 (single dose)

   i) Suggest why people living in Cornwall have a higher than normal dose.

   ....

   ii) Give **one** other natural source of background radiation.

   ....

   iii) A British pilot flies to Spain **and back** 500 times per year. If he
   lives in Cornwall, is his annual dose below the legal worker limit?

   ....

Atoms and Ionising Radiation

Q3 Match up each description with the correct type of radiation.

Alpha particle   2 neutrons and 2 protons — the same as a helium nucleus.

Beta particle   A type of electromagnetic radiation.

Gamma radiation   An electron from the nucleus.

Q4 Complete the table below by choosing the correct word from each column.

Radiation Type	Ionising power weak/ moderate/ strong	Charge positive/ none/ negative	Relative mass no mass/ small/large	Penetrating power low/moderate/ high	Range in air short/long/ very long
alpha					
beta					
gamma					

Q5 Write the nuclear equations for the following decay processes.

a) An atom of thorium-234 ($^{234}_{90}$Th) emits a beta particle and becomes an atom of protactinium (Pa).

....

b) An atom of radon-222 ($^{222}_{86}$Rn) emits an alpha particle and becomes an atom of polonium (Po).

....

Q6 The diagram to the right shows the paths of an alpha particle and beta particle in an **electric field**.

Identify **two** ways in which the path of the alpha and beta particle differ and **explain** the reason for each difference.

1. ....

....

....

2. ....

....

alpha particle

beta particle

96

Half-Life

Q1   A radioactive isotope has a half-life of **60 years**.
Which of these statements describes this isotope correctly? Tick one box only.

In 60 years, half of the atoms in the material will have gone. ☐

In 30 years' time, only half the atoms will be radioactive. ☐

In 60 years' time, the count rate will be half what it is now. ☐

In about 180 years there will be almost no radioactivity left in the material. ☐

Q2   The half-life of strontium-90 is **29 years**.

a) What does this tell you will have happened to a pure sample of strontium-90 in 29 years' time?

....

b) If you start with 1000 atoms of strontium-90, how many would you expect there to be after 87 years?

....

Q3   The activity of a radioactive sample is **1440 cpm**. 5 hours later
it has fallen to **45 cpm**. What is the half-life of this material?

....

....

Q4   Sandra measures how the radioactivity of a sample changes with time.
The table shows some of her results.

Time (minutes)	0	10	20	30	40	80	160
Counts per minute	740	553	420	326	260	140	103

a) Use Sandra's results to draw a graph of
counts per minute against time.

b) The counts per minute will never fall below 100.
Suggest two reasons why.

....

....

c) Sandra calculates that the half-life of her sample is
about 20 minutes. Explain how she worked this out.
(You may find it useful to show some of the working on your graph.)

....

....

Physics 2b — Electricity and the Atom

Uses of Radiation

Q1   The following sentences explain how a smoke detector works, but they are in the wrong order.

Put them in order by labelling them 1 (first) to 6 (last).

☐   The circuit is broken so no current flows.

[1]   The radioactive source emits alpha particles.

☐   A current flows between the electrodes — the alarm stays off.

☐   The alarm sounds.

☐   The air between the electrodes is ionised by the alpha particles.

☐   A fire starts and smoke particles absorb the alpha radiation.

Q2   The diagram shows how radiation can be used to sterilise surgical instruments.

radioactive source

thick lead

a)   What kind of radioactive source is used, and why? In your answer, mention the **type** of radiation emitted (α, β and γ) and the **half-life** of the source.

....

....

b)   What is the purpose of the thick lead?

....

Q3   The table shows the properties of three radioactive isotopes.

a)   Which isotope would be best to use as a medical tracer and why?

....

....

....

Radioactive isotope	Half-life	Type of emission
technetium-99	6 hours	beta/gamma
phosphorus-32	14 days	beta
cobalt-60	5 years	beta/gamma

b)   Which isotope would a hospital use to treat cancer patients? Explain your answer.

....

....

Radioactivity Safety

Q1 Two scientists are handling samples of radioactive material.

a) One of the scientists is taking sensible safety precautions, but the other is not.
Describe three things which the careless scientist is doing wrong.

1...

2...

3...

b) Describe another way the scientists can reduce their exposure to the radiation,
without using special apparatus or clothing.

....

....

c) How should radioactive samples be stored when they are not in use?

....

Q2 The three different types of radiation can all be dangerous.

a) Which **two** types of radiation can pass through the human body?
Circle the correct answers.

                alpha   beta   gamma

b) **i)** Which type of radiation is usually most dangerous if it's inhaled or swallowed?

....

ii) What effects can this type of radiation have on the human body?

....

....

....

Top Tips: You should always handle radioactive sources really carefully. People who work
with radioisotopes often wear **dosimeters** — badges which record their exposure.

Physics 2b — Electricity and the Atom

Nuclear Fission and Fusion

Q1 Choose from the following words to complete the passage.

| split | chemical | turbine | electricity | uranium-235 | water | wine |
| | | steam | moped | generator | reactors | heat |

Inside a nuclear reactor, ... (or plutonium-239) atoms

.... and release .... energy. This energy

is used to turn .... into ....

The steam then turns a ...., which in turn drives a

..................................., producing ....

Q2 Explain how a nuclear fission **chain reaction** occurs, starting with a single **plutonium** nucleus absorbing a **slow-moving neutron**.

....

....

....

....

Q3 List four differences between nuclear **fission** and nuclear **fusion**.

1...

2...

3...

4...

Q4 Give two good points and two bad points about **fusion reactors**.

Good points ....

....

Bad points ....

....

The Life Cycle of Stars

Q1   Complete the passage, choosing from the words given below.

gravity   millions   hot   fusion   stable   inwards   outwards   billions   fission   mass
When a protostar gets .... enough, hydrogen nuclei will start to undergo nuclear .... and the star enters its .... phase (becoming a main sequence star). The force from the heat generated inside the star (pushing ....) and the force of gravity (pushing ....) are balanced. The star might stay in this stable phase for .... of years.

Q2   Stars are formed from clouds of dust and gas.

a)   **Why** does the material come together?

....

b)   Describe how a **planets** can form around a star.

....

....

Q3   Towards the end of its life, a **main sequence** star will become a **red giant**.

a)   What causes a star to become a **red giant**?

....

....

b)   Why is a red giant **red**?

....

c)   What happens to **small stars** like our Sun after they become red giants?

....

....

Q4   Some red giants start to undergo **more fusion reactions**, glow very brightly and then **explode**. Give the **name** of this explosion, and describe what happens after it.

....

....

....

....

The Life Cycle of Stars

Q5   Below is a diagram showing the **life cycle** of **stars**.

Clouds of Dust and Gas
Red Giant
Neutron Star
Protostar
Black Hole
Main Sequence Star
Black Dwarf
White Dwarf
Supernova
Red Super Giant

Match the letters to the words on the right of the diagram.

A ....

B ....

C ....

D ....

E ....

F ....

G ....

H ....

I ....

J ....

Q6   The early universe only contained the element **hydrogen**.

a)   Why does the universe now contain lots of different elements?

....

b)   How are main sequence stars able to maintain their energy output for millions of years?

....

c)   Stars form heavy elements such as iron during their stable phases.
Describe how elements **heavier** than iron are created and **spread out** throughout the universe.

....

....

....

....

Mixed Questions — Physics 2b

Q1 The table gives information about four different **radioactive isotopes**.

Source	Type of Radiation	Half-life
radon-222	alpha	3.8 days
technetium-99m	gamma	6 hours
americium-241	alpha	432 years
cobalt-60	beta and gamma	5.27 years

a) Explain how the atomic structure of cobalt-60 is different from the structure of 'normal' cobalt-59.

....

....

b) Which sources in the table would be most suitable for each of the uses below?

  medical tracers   **smoke detectors**   **detecting leaks in pipes**

  ....

c) Radiation can be used to treat cancer.

  i) What type of radiation is used in this treatment? ....

  ii) Explain why patients often feel very ill while receiving this treatment.

    ....

    ....

d) Jim measures the count rate of a sample of americium-241 as 120 cpm.
  Roughly how long would it take for the count rate to fall below **4 cpm**? Show your working.

  ....

  ....

e) Give **two** precautions Jim should take while handling the radioactive sample.

  1. ....

  2. ....

Top Tips: These mixed questions are like a good quality pick 'n' mix — there's a bit of everything in there: radioactive half-life, stars and electricity... And that's just what the exam'll be like.

Mixed Questions — Physics 2b

Q2   The diagram below shows part of a chain reaction in a nuclear reactor.

a)   What is the name of the type of radioactive decay shown in the diagram? ....

b)   This decay happens as part of a chain reaction. Describe what happens in this chain reaction.

....

....

....

c)   Describe how thermal energy from the reactor is used to generate electricity.

....

....

Electricity can also be generated using energy released from **nuclear fusion**.

d)   Give two advantages of producing electricity using **fusion** rather than the reaction shown above.

1. ....

2. ....

e)   Explain why nuclear fusion isn't widely used to generate electricity.

....

....

f)   Nuclear fusion is the process by which energy is released in **stars**.

i)   Explain why the universe now contains less hydrogen than it used to.

....

....

ii)   The **forces** within a star are **balanced** during the **main sequence** period of its life cycle
Explain the role of **fusion** in this.

....

....

Mixed Questions — Physics 2b

Q3   Modern electrical appliances are carefully designed to prevent the user getting an electric shock.

a) Tom's washing machine develops a fault. Part of the live wire touches the metal case.
Explain how the earth wire and fuse work together to prevent Tom getting an electric shock.

....

....

b) Bob buys a new 'double insulated' television set.

i) Which wires are in the plug?   ....

ii) What is meant by 'double insulated'?

....

Q4   Kate charges her mobile phone using a mobile phone charger, rated at 230 V, 600 W.

a) The battery in the mobile phone supplies a direct current (DC).
Explain what is meant by direct current.

....

b) Work out whether a 2.5 A, 3 A or 6 A fuse would be best to use in the phone charger.

....

c) The plastic casing on the plug for Kate's charger has broken.
Explain why Kate shouldn't use the mobile phone charger.

....

....

d) A mobile phone battery supplies direct current (DC) but mains electricity is alternating current (AC).

The diagram shows a CRO trace from a mains electricity supply on the
island of Bezique. The **timebase** dial was set to 10 ms per large division.

Calculate the **frequency** of Bezique's electricity supply.

....

....

X-rays in Medicine

Q1 In each of the following sentences, circle the correct word(s) from each highlighted pair.

a) X-rays are **short / long** wavelength electromagnetic
waves that can cause **refraction / ionisation**.

b) X-rays are **transmitted / absorbed** by healthy soft tissue but are
transmitted / absorbed by dense materials such as bone.

c) Electronic images can be formed using a **photographic film / charge-coupled device**.

d) The wavelength of an X-ray is roughly the same as the diameter of a **car / cell / atom**.

Q2 Complete the following paragraph using the words provided.

ill	centre	normal	kill	cells	focused	cancer	rotating

High doses of X-ray radiation will .... living ....

Because of this, X-rays are used to treat .... X-rays are ....

on the tumour using a wide beam. Damage to .... cells can make the

patient feel very .... This damage is minimised by ....

the X-ray beam, keeping the tumour at the ....

Q3 X-ray images can be used to **diagnose** medical conditions.

a) Describe how X-ray images can be formed using **photographic film**.

....

....

....

....

b) Briefly describe how X-ray images can be formed **electronically**.

....

....

....

c) Name one medical condition that X-rays can be used to diagnose.

....

X-rays in Medicine

Q4 Tick the boxes to show whether each of these statements is **true** or **false**.

True **False**

a) The images created using CT scans have a high resolution. ☐ ☐

b) Only soft tissue can be imaged by CT scans. ☐ ☐

c) CT scans use less X-ray radiation than traditional X-ray imaging. ☐ ☐

d) A drawback of CT scanning is its use of ionising radiation. ☐ ☐

Q5 When a CT scan is taken, an image is produced by a computer. Order the statements below 1 to 5 to describe the process of taking a CT scan. The first one has been done for you.

☐ An X-ray tube emits an X-ray beam whilst rotating around the patient.

☐ Multiple slice images are put together to give a three-dimensional picture.

☐ A computer uses the detected X-rays to generate an image of a two-dimensional slice through the body.

☐ Detectors on the opposite side of the scanner measure the intensity of transmitted X-rays.

1 The patient is put inside the CT scanner.

Q6 When radiographers take X-ray 'photographs' or scans of patients, they themselves are exposed to X-rays.

a) Write down **two precautions** radiographers can take to minimise their exposure to X-rays.

1. ....

2. ....

b) Describe **two** ways in which the patient's radiation dose can be **minimised**.

1. ....

....

2. ....

....

Top Tips: In a CT scan, the image is built up by the subtle differences in different tissues' ability to block the X-ray beam. Because lots of 2D 'slice' images are created, there's no problem of different body parts getting in the way of each other like there is in an X-ray — you get the complete picture.

Ultrasound

Q1   Ultrasound imaging can be used to diagnose soft tissue problems.

    a)   What is ultrasound?

    ....

    b)   How can ultrasound of a particular frequency be generated?

    ....

    ....

Q2   Ultrasound can be used to detect the existence of a different medium below the surface of an object, and to measure how far below the surface it is.

    Sketch a diagram showing what happens when an ultrasound wave hits the boundary between one medium and another.

Q3   A layer of **fat** sitting between a layer of **skin** and a layer of **muscle** is examined using **ultrasound**. The **oscilloscope trace** below shows two pulses of ultrasound from the examination — the first pulse is reflected off the layer of fat and the second is reflected off the layer of muscle. Each **time division** on the oscilloscope represents **5 µs** and the speed of sound through tissue is **1450 m/s**.

    a)   Calculate the distance from the ultrasound device to the layer of fat.

              1 µs = 0.000001 s

       ....

       ....

       ....

    b)   Use the oscilloscope trace to calculate the **thickness of the layer of fat**. Give your answer in centimetres and to one decimal place.

    ....

    ....

    ....

Ultrasound Uses

Q1 A concentrated beam of **ultrasound** can be used to treat kidney stones.

a) What effect does the ultrasound beam have on kidney stones?

....

b) How are the kidney stone remains removed from the body?

....

c) Give two reasons why using ultrasound is a good way of treating kidney stones.

1. ....

2. ....

Q2 Doctors use different imaging techniques to diagnose different medical conditions.

a) Fill in the table below with **one advantage** and **one disadvantage** of ultrasound, X-rays and CT scans.

	Advantage	Disadvantage
Ultrasound imaging		
X-ray photographs		
CT scans		

b) Which medical imaging technique would you recommend for the planning of complicated brain surgery? Explain your answer

....

....

Q3 Ultrasound can be used in a similar way to **X-rays**.

a) Why is ultrasound safer than X-rays?

....

b) State whether X-rays or ultrasound would be used to investigate a suspected broken bone, and explain why.

....

....

....

Refractive Index

Q1 The diagram below shows light entering a glass block.

a) As the light enters the glass block it changes direction. What is the name of this effect?

....

b) Complete the diagram to show the ray passing through the block and emerging from the other side. Include labels A to E for:

A   the refracted ray

B   the emergent ray

C   the normal for the emergent ray

D   the angle of incidence

E   the angle of refraction

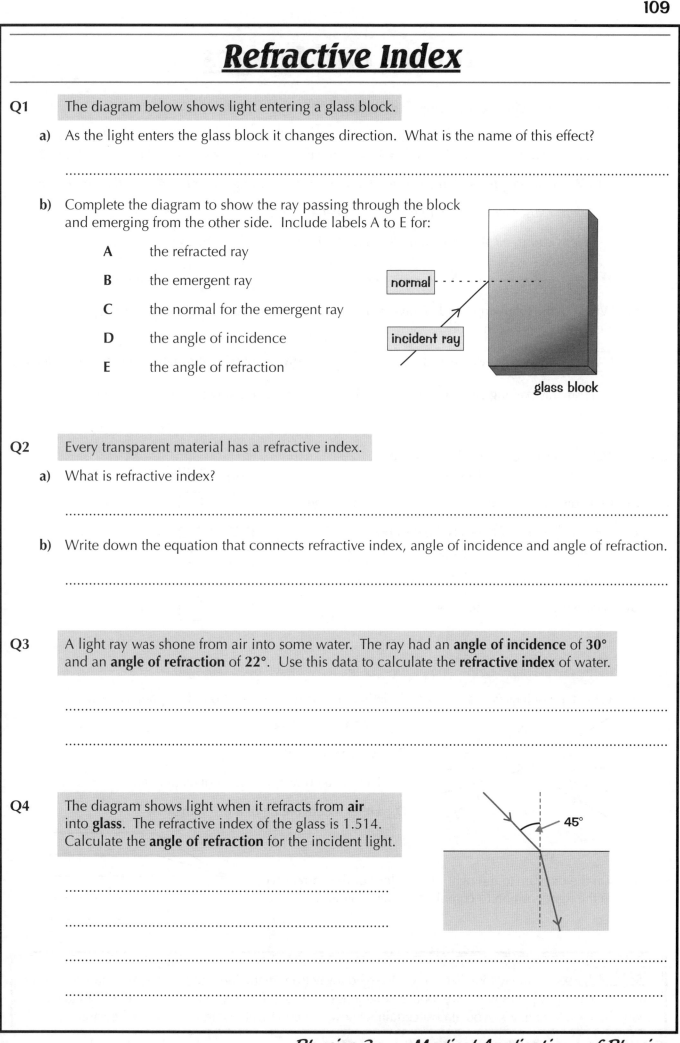

Q2 Every transparent material has a refractive index.

a) What is refractive index?

....

b) Write down the equation that connects refractive index, angle of incidence and angle of refraction.

....

Q3 A light ray was shone from air into some water. The ray had an **angle of incidence** of **30°** and an **angle of refraction** of **22°**. Use this data to calculate the **refractive index** of water.

....

....

Q4 The diagram shows light when it refracts from **air** into **glass**. The refractive index of the glass is 1.514. Calculate the **angle of refraction** for the incident light.

....

....

....

....

Lenses and Images

Q1   Lenses can be either **converging** or **diverging**.

a)   In the following sentences the words **parallel**, **converging**, **principal focus** and **incident** have been replaced by the letters **W**, **X**, **Y**, **Z**. Write down which words are represented by **W**, **X**, **Y** and **Z**.

*An **W** ray passing through the centre of a **X** lens from any angle carries on in the same direction.*

*A **X** lens causes all **W** rays **Y** to the axis to meet at the **Z**.*

*A **X** lens causes all **W** rays passing through the **Z** to emerge **Y** to the axis.*

W ....   X ....   Y ....   Z ....

b)   Which of the following incident rays do not have their direction changed by either type of lens?
Tick any boxes which apply.

☐ Any ray parallel to the axis   ☐ Any ray passing through the centre of the lens

☐ Any ray passing along the axis   ☐ Any ray passing through the principal focus

Q2   Tick the boxes to show whether each of these statements is **true** or **false**.

	True	False
a) Only diverging lenses can produce a virtual image.	☐	☐
b) The focal length of a lens is the distance from the centre of the lens to the principal focus.	☐	☐
c) A real image can be projected on a screen	☐	☐
d) A converging lens is concave.	☐	☐

Q3   In the ray diagrams below, the pictures of the lenses have been removed.

a)   What type of lens could this be? Underline the correct answer from the options below.

Lens here

A   A converging lens

B   A diverging lens

C   Neither a converging nor a diverging lens

D   Either a converging or a diverging lens

b)   On the diagram to the right, draw a lens of the correct type in the right position to complete the ray diagram.

> ### Top Tips: It may look like we've diverged away from medicine, but fear not, we shall converge on it again in a few pages when we look at what lenses are used for. If you can't guess what I'm talking about, here's a little hint — you almost certainly know someone who wears a pair (and they aren't pants).

Lenses and Images

Q4　Images formed by lenses can either be **real** or **virtual**.

a)　What is the difference between a real and a virtual image?

....

....

b)　What **three** pieces of information do you need to give to describe the nature of an image?

1. ....

2. ....

3. ....

Q5　This question is about how to **draw ray diagrams** for **converging lenses**.

a)　The first step is to draw a ray from the **top** of the object going **parallel** to the **axis** of the lens. Where does this ray pass through when it's refracted?

....

b)　The next step is to draw a ray from the top of the object which passes through the lens **without** being refracted. Where does this ray pass through the lens?

....

c)　How do the steps above tell you where the **top** of the **image** will be on the ray diagram?

....

Q6　The diagram shows a **diverging lens**.

a)　Draw the path of a ray passing through the lens **along the axis** from left to right.

b)　Draw the paths of two incident rays **parallel** to the first ray, one **above** and one **below** the axis.

c)　Sketch in the position of the **virtual principal focus** for the rays shown and label it "F".

Lenses

Q1 Some of this diagram has been hidden. Draw in the rest of the diagram, showing the position of the **object** that produced the image you see.

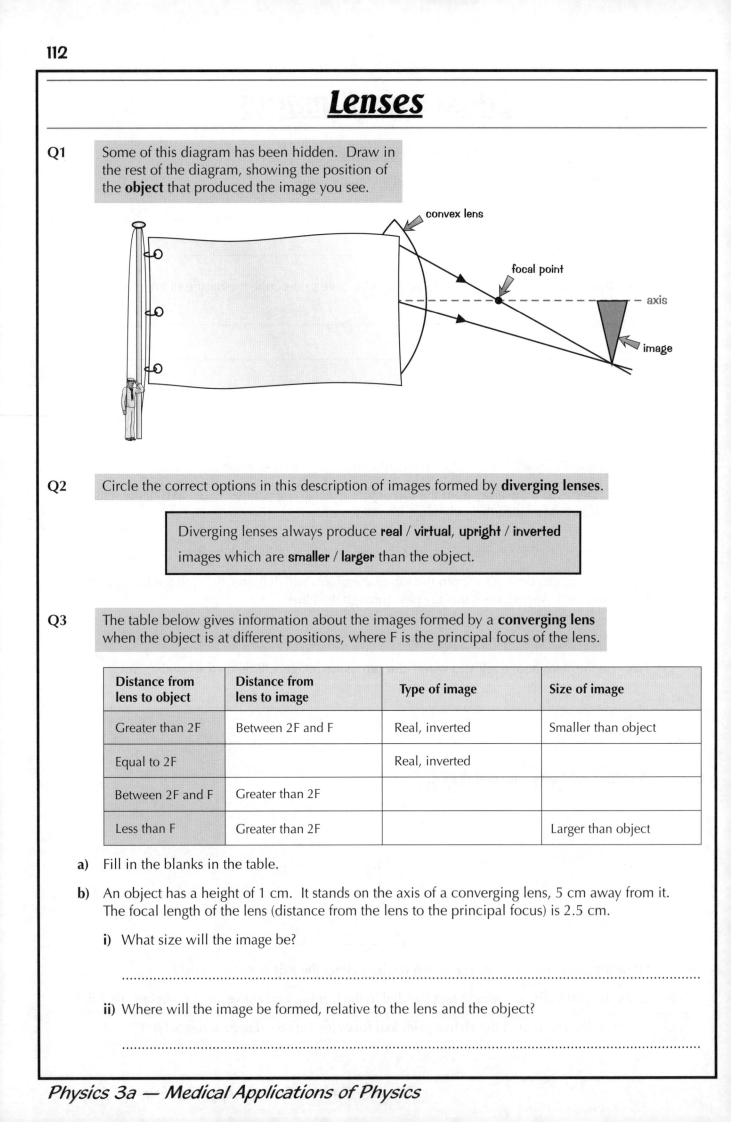

Q2 Circle the correct options in this description of images formed by **diverging lenses**.

Diverging lenses always produce **real** / **virtual**, **upright** / **inverted** images which are **smaller** / **larger** than the object.

Q3 The table below gives information about the images formed by a **converging lens** when the object is at different positions, where F is the principal focus of the lens.

Distance from lens to object	Distance from lens to image	Type of image	Size of image
Greater than 2F	Between 2F and F	Real, inverted	Smaller than object
Equal to 2F		Real, inverted	
Between 2F and F	Greater than 2F		
Less than F	Greater than 2F		Larger than object

a) Fill in the blanks in the table.

b) An object has a height of 1 cm. It stands on the axis of a converging lens, 5 cm away from it. The focal length of the lens (distance from the lens to the principal focus) is 2.5 cm.

  i) What size will the image be?

  ....

  ii) Where will the image be formed, relative to the lens and the object?

  ....

Physics 3a — Medical Applications of Physics

Lenses

Q4 An aubergine is placed **6.1 cm** away from a converging lens with a focal length of **7 cm**.

a) Will the image formed by the lens be:

i) upright or inverted? ....

ii) on the same side of the lens or on the opposite side? ....

iii) real or virtual? ....

b) The aubergine is now placed at a distance x from the lens. The image is now bigger than the object and inverted. Which of the options below could be distance x? Circle your answer.

    A 3.9 cm   **B 7.0 cm**   **C 10.2 cm**   **D 14.0 cm**   **E 15.3 cm**

Q5 The diagram below shows an object placed next to a diverging lens. The locations of each principal focus are marked F.

a) On the diagram, draw the path of a ray coming from the top of the object and travelling in the direction of the centre of the lens.

b) Draw the path of a ray coming from the top of the object and going towards the lens parallel to the axis.

c) Draw the image formed by the lens.

Q6 Complete the ray diagram below to show the image produced by the lens.

Top Tips: Aubergines aside, you'll be expected to know how to draw lovely ray diagrams for converging and diverging lenses. They can be a bit tricky, but examiners love 'em, so get practising.

Magnification and Power

Q1 Mr Richards is using a **magnifying glass** to read a magazine by the light of an overhead lamp.

a) What sort of lens is used in a magnifying glass?

....

b) Explain why an object you want to view with a magnifying glass must be placed nearer to the lens than the principal focus.

....

....

c) The writing on the magazine is in focus when the lens is a distance of 9 cm or less from the magazine. When the magnifying glass is held exactly 26 cm from the magazine a sharply focused image of the light bulb appears on the magazine.

Three of the following statements are **true**. Circle the appropriate letters.

A	The lens works as a magnifying glass when it is held anywhere nearer than 26 cm to the magazine.
B	The lens works as a magnifying glass when it is held anywhere nearer than 9 cm to the magazine.
C	The focal length of the lens is 26 cm.
D	The focal length of the lens is 9 cm.
E	The image of the light bulb projected onto the magazine is a real image.
F	The image of the light bulb projected onto the magazine is a virtual image.

Q2 The magnification of a magnifying glass depends on the distance of the object from the lens.

a) State the formula for the magnification produced by a lens or mirror.

....

b) A handwriting expert is studying a handwritten letter "A" with a magnifying glass. The letter is 0.5 cm high. When a magnifying glass is held 10 cm from the letter, the image of the letter appears to be 0.8 cm high. What is the magnification of the glass at that distance?

....

c) The same magnifying glass is used to look at a ring made from a strip of gold of width 3 mm. The ring is also held 10 cm from the glass. How wide will the image be?

....

heh
heh
heh...

Magnification and Power

Q3 Convex lenses can also be called **converging lenses**.

thinner lenses *fatter lenses*

a) Which lenses are more powerful? Circle the correct answer.

b) Write out the equation that relates lens power to focal length.

....

Q4 Dave is using a converging lens to **focus** some parallel rays of light to a point.

a) If the distance between the centre of the lens, X, and the principal focus, Y, is 15 cm, what is the power of the lens?

....

b) Dave wants to increase the distance between the lens and the principal focus, so he switches the lens for one with a power of 5.2 D. Calculate the new distance between X and Y.

....

c) How is the power of a **diverging** lens different to that of a **converging** lens?

....

Q5 Nanny Irene goes to the opticians to get some new glasses.

a) What **two** factors determine the focal length of a lens?

1. ....

2. ....

b) Despite the focal length of her eyes staying the same, Nanny Irene gets new glasses with **thinner** lenses than before. Explain how the manufacturers of her glasses achieved this.

....

....

....

The Eye

Q1   Add labels to complete the diagram of the eye below.

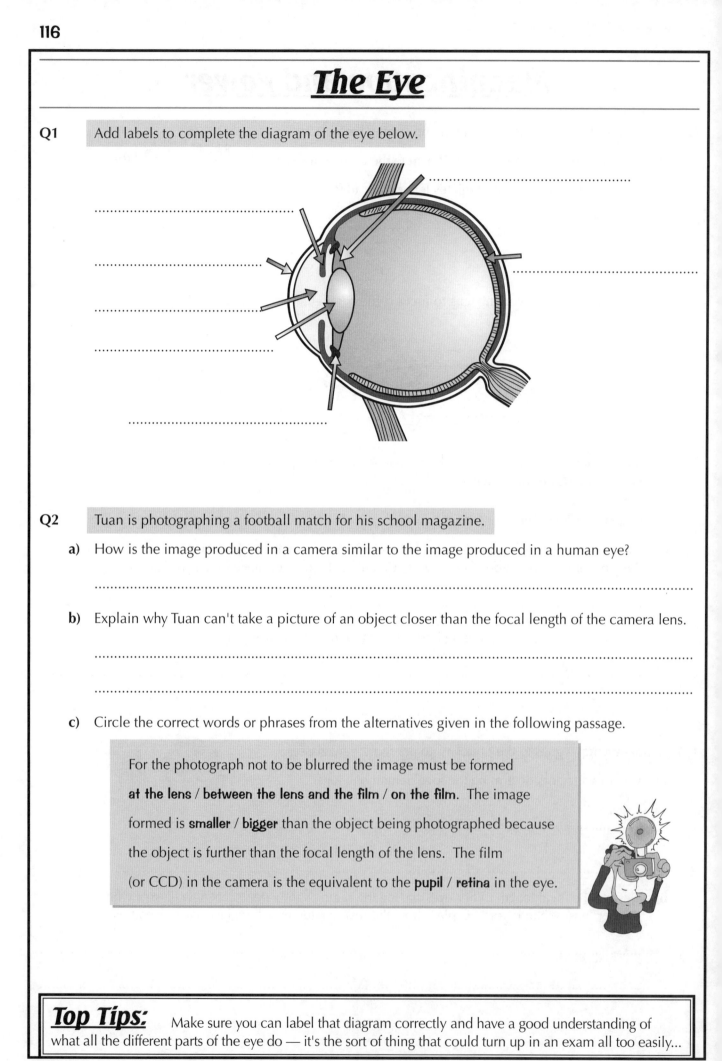

Q2   Tuan is photographing a football match for his school magazine.

a)   How is the image produced in a camera similar to the image produced in a human eye?

....

b)   Explain why Tuan can't take a picture of an object closer than the focal length of the camera lens.

....

....

c)   Circle the correct words or phrases from the alternatives given in the following passage.

For the photograph not to be blurred the image must be formed

at the lens / between the lens and the film / on the film. The image

formed is **smaller / bigger** than the object being photographed because

the object is further than the focal length of the lens. The film

(or CCD) in the camera is the equivalent to the **pupil / retina** in the eye.

Top Tips: Make sure you can label that diagram correctly and have a good understanding of
what all the different parts of the eye do — it's the sort of thing that could turn up in an exam all too easily...

The Eye

Q3   **Complete the table** about the functions of different parts of the eye.

Part of the eye	Function
....	Focuses light on the retina
Retina	....
Ciliary muscles	....
....	Hole through which light enters the eye

Q4   Circle the correct word in each pair to complete the passage below.

> When you look at distant objects, your ciliary muscles **contract** / **relax**, and pull the lens to make it **thin** / **fat**. The opposite actions happen when you look at near objects. The combined action of the lens and **cornea** / **iris** focuses the light on the **pupil** / **retina** to produce an image. Cells on the **pupil** / **retina** send signals to the brain to be interpreted via the optic nerve.

Q5   The range of human eyesight lies between the **near** and **far points**.
Complete the definitions of near and far points below.

a)   The near point is ....

For normally-sighted adults, the near point is about .... cm.

b)   The far point is ....

For normally-sighted adults, the far point is at ....

Correcting Vision

Q1 Common vision problems are caused by the eye focusing an image in the wrong place.

a) Look at the image on the right. Complete the sentences by choosing the correct word(s) from the highlighted options.

The person with this vision defect is **short / long** sighted.

The **near / far** point is closer than infinity, which makes it

difficult to focus on things that are **close up / far away**. The object

in the diagram is brought into focus **in front of / behind** the retina.

object

b) Give **two** possible causes of the problem shown in the diagram.

1. ....

2. ....

c) **i)** Which of the two lenses shown on the right could correct this problem? Circle the correct letter.

A   B

ii) Explain how the lens you chose in part **c)i)** would help to correct the eye problem.

....

....

....

Q2 **Lasers** are increasingly used in surgery.

a) What is a laser?

....

b) Lasers can cut, cauterise and burn tissue.

i) Explain what cauterisation means.

....

ii) Briefly describe how a surgeon can use a laser to correct long or short sight.

....

....

....

Top Tips: Corrective lenses can be in the form of spectacles **or** contact lenses — which ones you wear is up to you. Remember, both can be either diverging or converging lenses. Good 'ol lenses.

Total Internal Reflection

Q1 Doctors can use an **endoscope**, a thin tube containing **optical fibres**, to look inside a patient's body.

a) What type of radiation is sent along optical fibres?

....

b) What material could the optical fibres in the endoscope be made from?

....

c) Explain why endoscopes contain two bundles of optical fibres.

....

....

d) Optical fibres work because of repeated **total internal reflections**.
Complete the ray diagrams below. The critical angle for glass/air is 42°.

air
glass

air
glass

You'll need to measure the angle of incidence for each one — carefully.

Q2 Martin wants to buy a ring for Marion. He compares a **diamond** ring with a **glass** imitation ring.

a) The critical angle between glass and air is **42°**. Calculate the refractive index of glass.

....

b) Martin knows that the refractive index of diamond is **2.4**.
Calculate the critical angle between diamond and air.

....

c) The glass imitation ring is cut in exactly the same way as the diamond ring.
Which of the two rings will be the most **sparkly**?
Explain your answer using your answers from parts **a)** and **b)**.

Think about how much light will be reflected.

....

....

....

....

Mixed Questions — Physics 3a

Q1 Lara is having a great time investigating how light travels through media.

a) Lara shines a ray of light passing across the **boundary** between two media.

Medium 1	Medium 2

i) Which of Medium 1 and Medium 2 is air and which is glass?

Medium 1 is .... Medium 2 is ....

ii) Explain your answer to **a) i)**. ....

....

....

b) **i)** In which of these situations could Lara get total internal reflection? Circle the correct letter(s).

   A Light is travelling from air into water.
   B Light is travelling from glass into air.

ii) Explain your answer to **b) i)**. ....

....

....

c) Lara investigates refraction of light in water by shining a beam of light **up** through a fish tank to the air above. She finds the **critical angle** of light travelling from water into air is **49°**.

i) Calculate the refractive index of water.

....

....

ii) She shines the beam of light down into the water from the air at an angle of 20°.
Use your answer from part **c) i)** to calculate the angle of refraction of the light.

....

....

....

Mixed Questions — Physics 3a

Q2   Andrew and Cassie are looking at a shell.
They can see it because images **form on their retinas**.

a)   Complete the paths of the light rays on the diagram below so that
the image of the shell is correctly brought into focus on the retina.

b)   The light entering Cassie's eye is shown in the
diagram to the right. Her lens is working correctly.

Circle the correct words to complete the sentences below.

> Cassie's eyeball is too **long / short,** so images form **behind / in front of** her retina.
>
> This can be corrected by **concave / convex** spectacle lenses as these make light rays converge.

c)   Cassie wears glasses to correct her vision.
The lens for her right eye has a focal length of **0.4 m**.

i)   Calculate the **power** of the lens.

....

ii)   The lens for her left eye is made of the **same material** as the lens for her right eye,
but has a **higher power**. Describe how the two lenses will differ in appearance.

....

d)   Andrew uses a **magnifying glass** to examine the shell, which is **1.8 cm** tall.
He finds that to magnify the shell, he must hold the lens less than **3 cm** from it.
When he holds the magnifying glass **2.5 cm** away from the shell, the image formed is **4 cm** tall.

i)   What is the focal length of this lens?

....

ii)   What is the magnification of the lens at 2.5 cm?

....

iii) Is the image real or virtual? Explain your answer.

....

....

Mixed Questions — Physics 3a

Q3   **Ultrasound imaging** is a valuable technique in many different medical investigations.

a) A pulse of ultrasound is directed toward an unborn fetus. It **partially reflects** when it reaches the amniotic fluid and again when it reaches the body of the fetus. An oscilloscope trace shows that the time between the reflected pulses is **26 μs**. The speed of sound through the fluid is 1500 m/s. Calculate how far the fetus is from the outside of the amniotic fluid.

....

....

....

Remember — when something is reflected, the distance it has travelled is there and back.

b) Explain why ultrasound is used in pre-natal scans instead of X-rays.

....

....

c) X-rays can be used to treat cancer, but ultrasound can't. Explain why.

....

....

d) CT scans can produce very clear images of inside the body, but doctors always try to keep their use to an absolute minimum. Explain why doctors will only take CT scans when it is absolutely necessary.

....

....

e) Describe the process of producing a **three-dimensional CT image**. Include the words in the box below in your answer.

| X-ray tube | slice | detectors | rotated | computer |

....

....

....

....

....

Top Tips: Examiners love to ask questions that get you to show that you really know what you're talking about — and a good example is getting you to compare the different medical imaging processes. Make sure you are totally clued up on the pros and cons of X-rays, ultrasound and CT scans.

Turning Forces and the Centre of Mass

Q1 a) Fill in the blanks in the following passage, using the words supplied.

pivot	perpendicular	moment	force

The turning effect of a .... is called its ....

It can be found by multiplying the force by the .... distance from

the line of action of the force to the ....

b) What are the units in which moments are measured? ....

Q2 To open a door, its handle needs to be **rotated clockwise**.

a) A force of 45 N is exerted vertically downwards on the door-handle at
a distance of 0.1 m from the pivot. What is the **moment** of the force?

0.1 m

45 N

....

b) Pictures **A**, **B**, **C** and **D** show equal forces being exerted on the handle.

A   **B**   **C**   **D**

Which of the forces shown (**A**, **B**, **C** or **D**) exerts:

i) the largest moment? ....   **ii)** the smallest moment? ....

Q3 A baby's pram toy consists of a toy banana hanging from a bar over the pram.

a) The banana is hanging **at rest**, as shown.
Draw a line on which the centre of mass **must** fall.

b) Complete the following sentences by choosing from the words and phrases below:

level with	vertically below	perpendicular	moment	centre of mass	horizontal

When a suspended object's .... is ....

the pivot, the .... distance between the line of action of the

gravitational force and the pivot is zero. This means that there is no

.... due to the object's weight.

Turning Forces and the Centre of Mass

Q4   You can think of the **centre of mass** as the point where all the mass of an object seems to be concentrated.

a)   Using lines of symmetry, find the centre of mass of each of these shapes:

b)   **Circle** the correct answer to complete this sentence.
The centre of mass of a raindrop is:

A   at the top

B   near the top

C   midway down

D   near the bottom

E   at the bottom

Q5   Two men, one at each end, hold a 0.8 m long metal pole weighing 130 N so that it is in a **horizontal** position. One man accidentally lets go of his end.

First, find the centre of mass of the pole.

What is the moment on the pole due to its weight an instant after he lets go?

Draw a diagram.

....

....

....

Q6   Some pupils want to find the centre of mass of an **irregularly shaped** piece of cardboard. They are equipped with a stand to hang the card from, a plumb line and a pencil. They make a hole near one edge of the card and hang it from the stand.

a)   What steps should they take next in order to find the centre of mass?

....

....

....

....

b)   How could they make their result more reliable?

....

....

Balanced Moments and Levers

Q1 A 2 N weight (Weight A) sits 20 cm to the left of the pivot of a balance.
A 5 N weight (Weight B) is placed 16 cm to the left of the pivot.

a) What is the moment exerted by **Weight A**? ....

b) What is the moment exerted by **Weight B**? ....

c) How far to the right of the pivot should Weight C (8 N) be placed to **balance** A and B?

....

....

d) If all three of the weights were exactly **twice as far** away from the pivot,
would the balance tip over to one side? Explain your answer.

....

Q2 Barbara uses a wheelbarrow to move things around her allotment.
She says "I love my wheelbarrow. It makes it so much easier to lift everything."

Explain **how** a wheelbarrow reduces the
amount of force needed to lift an object.

Hint: a wheelbarrow is
just a type of lever.

....

....

....

....

Q3 One side of a drop-leaf table is pivoted on a hinge
and supported 5 cm from its edge by a table leg.
The table leaf is 80 cm long and weighs 40 N.

Find the force, F, exerted by the table leg (when the
table leaf is fully extended).

....

....

....

Moments, Stability and Pendulums

Q1 The top drawer of a two-drawer filing cabinet is full of heavy files, but the bottom drawer is empty.

Why is the cabinet in danger of falling over if the top drawer is fully pulled out?

....

....

....

Q2 The pictures show three different designs for **vases**.

A   B   C

Which vase will be **most stable**? Explain your answer.

....

....

Q3 The diagram to the right shows a cart being used to carry coal along a slope. The centre of mass of the cart, when full, is shown.

Centre of mass

a) Explain why the cart **doesn't** topple over when on the slope.

....

....

b) Suggest **one** way in which the stability of the cart could be improved.

....

Q4 A magician is using a pendulum to practise hypnotism. The pendulum swings with a time period of 1.25 s.

a) Calculate the frequency of the pendulum.

....

....

b) The magician decides the time period of the pendulum's swing needs to be longer to work best. Suggest **one** way in which he could increase the time period of the pendulum.

....

> **Top Tips:** In the exam, you might be expected to look at an object and describe how its design affects its stability. You're always looking for the same sort of things though — where its centre of mass is and how wide its base is. My massive bottom means I'm fairly stable and very difficult to topple.

Hydraulics

Q1 Fill in the blanks in the following passage, using the words supplied.

transmitted	force	equally	incompressible	pressure	flow

Liquids can .... and are virtually .... These
properties mean that a .... exerted at one point on a liquid will be
.... to other points in the liquid. .... can also
be transmitted through a liquid — it is transmitted .... in all directions.

Q2 The diagram on the right shows a **simple hydraulic system**.

a) Hydraulic systems are used as '**force multipliers**'.
Briefly describe how a hydraulic system works as a 'force multiplier'.

....

....

....

....

b) A force of 650 N is applied to the 1st piston, which has a cross-sectional area of 0.0025 m².

i) Calculate the pressure created in the liquid by the first piston.

....

ii) What will the pressure of the liquid at the 2nd piston be? Explain your answer.

....

....

Q3 The diagram below shows two syringes connected by a tube. The entire system is filled with water. When a **force** is applied to one syringe, water passes through the tube to the other syringe.

A force of 18 N is applied to the piston of the small syringe.

a) Calculate the pressure created by the force.

....

....

b) Calculate the force acting on the piston of the larger syringe.

....

....

Circular Motion

Q1 Which of the following is the **best explanation** of acceleration? Circle the appropriate letter.

A an increase in speed

D a change in velocity

B a change in direction

E a change in speed

C an increase in velocity

Q2 The diagram below shows a clock with hands that move **steadily** around the clock-face.

a) Draw and label with 'A' an arrow on the diagram to show the direction of the **velocity** of the tip of the **minute hand**.

b) Draw and label with 'B' an arrow to show the direction of the **acceleration** of the tip of the **hour hand**.

Q3 A **satellite** orbiting the Earth travels at a constant speed.

a) Is the satellite accelerating? Explain your answer.

....

b) Put a tick next to each true statement below.

☐ "If a body is accelerating then there must be a resultant force acting on it."

☐ "The forces acting on a body going round in a circle at a steady speed must be balanced."

☐ "If there is no resultant force acting on a body then it carries on moving in a straight line at the same speed."

c) What is the general name for a force that keeps a body moving in a circular path?

....

d) Draw lines to match up the following bodies with the force that keeps them moving in a circle.

A runner running round a circular track	Gravity
A satellite in orbit round the Earth	Tension
The seats at the ends of the spokes of a spinning fairground ride	Friction

Q4 Circle the correct options in these sentences.

a) The greater the mass of a body, the **smaller / greater** the force needed to keep it moving in a circle.

b) The faster the speed of a body, the **smaller / greater** the force needed to keep it moving in a circle.

c) A cyclist rides round a circular track at a speed of 20 m/s.
The frictional force between his tyres and the track is 1467 N.
He speeds up to 21 m/s — the frictional force changes to **1617 N / 1331 N**.

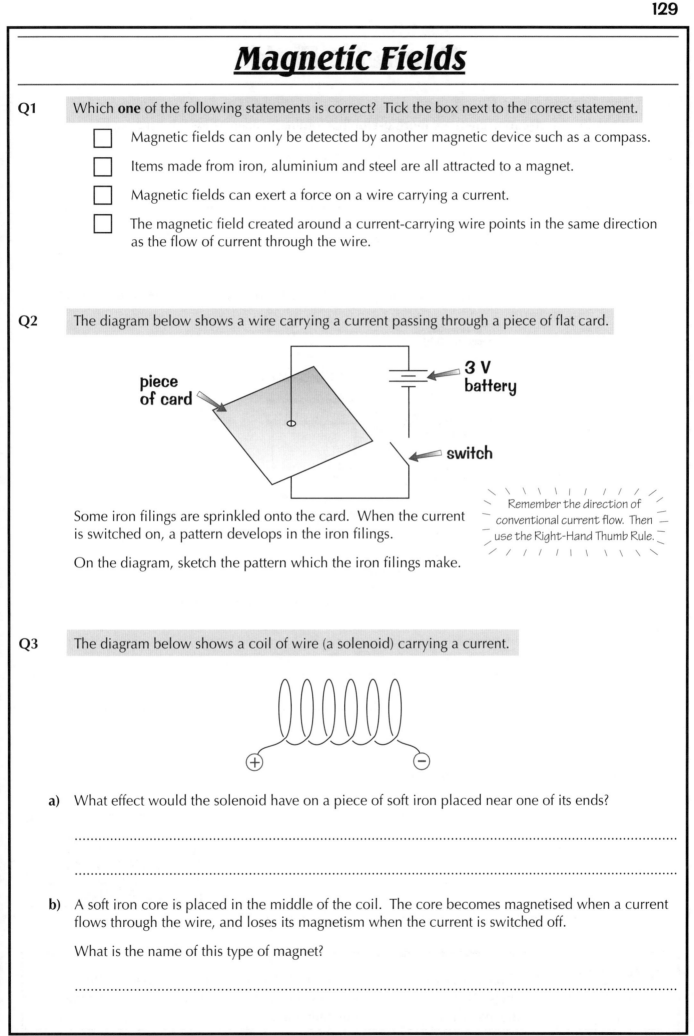

Magnetic Fields

Q1 Which **one** of the following statements is correct? Tick the box next to the correct statement.

☐ Magnetic fields can only be detected by another magnetic device such as a compass.

☐ Items made from iron, aluminium and steel are all attracted to a magnet.

☐ Magnetic fields can exert a force on a wire carrying a current.

☐ The magnetic field created around a current-carrying wire points in the same direction as the flow of current through the wire.

Q2 The diagram below shows a wire carrying a current passing through a piece of flat card.

piece of card

3 V battery

switch

Some iron filings are sprinkled onto the card. When the current is switched on, a pattern develops in the iron filings.

Remember the direction of conventional current flow. Then use the Right-Hand Thumb Rule.

On the diagram, sketch the pattern which the iron filings make.

Q3 The diagram below shows a coil of wire (a solenoid) carrying a current.

$+$ $-$

a) What effect would the solenoid have on a piece of soft iron placed near one of its ends?

....

....

b) A soft iron core is placed in the middle of the coil. The core becomes magnetised when a current flows through the wire, and loses its magnetism when the current is switched off.

What is the name of this type of magnet?

....

__Magnetic Fields__

Q4   Electromagnets are often found in cranes used for lifting iron and steel.
Explain why electromagnets are **more useful** than ordinary magnets for this purpose.

....

....

....

Q5   The diagram shows how a solenoid can be used as a relay to switch an external circuit on and off.

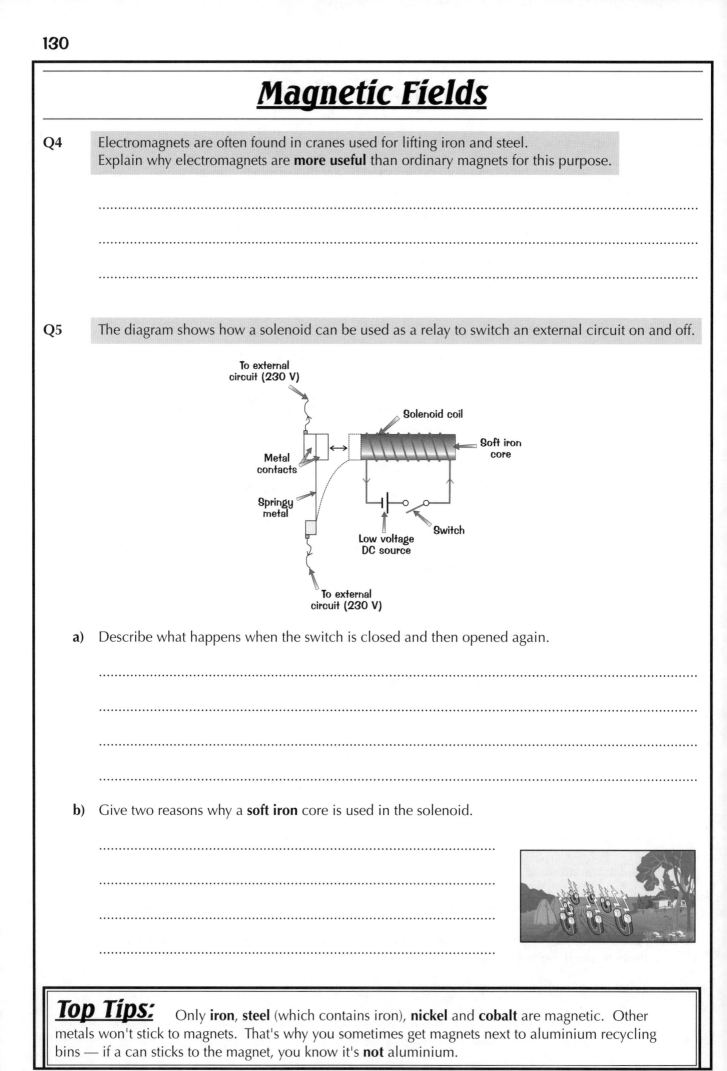

a)   Describe what happens when the switch is closed and then opened again.

....

....

....

....

b)   Give two reasons why a **soft iron** core is used in the solenoid.

....

....

....

....

___

Top Tips: Only **iron**, **steel** (which contains iron), **nickel** and **cobalt** are magnetic. Other metals won't stick to magnets. That's why you sometimes get magnets next to aluminium recycling bins — if a can sticks to the magnet, you know it's **not** aluminium.

The Motor Effect

Q1 Complete the passage below using the words supplied.

force	angle	stronger	current	magnetic field	motor	permanent magnets

A wire carrying an electric current has a .... around it. This

can interact with the magnetic fields of other wires or of ....

to produce a .... and sometimes movement. A bigger .... or a

.... magnet will produce a bigger force. The size of the force will also depend on

the .... at which the two magnetic fields meet each other. A force is experienced

by a current-carrying wire in a magnetic field — this is known as the .... effect.

Q2 The diagram shows an electrical wire between two magnetic poles.
When the current is switched on, the wire moves at right angles
to the magnetic field.

a) Using Fleming's Left-Hand Rule, state which way the wire will move.

....

b) How could the wire be made to move in the opposite direction?

....

Q3 Read the three statements below. Tick the box next to each statement that you think is **true**.

☐ A current-carrying wire will not experience a force if it is parallel to the
magnetic field of a permanent magnet.

☐ A current-carrying wire will not experience a force if it is at right-angles
to the magnetic field of a permanent magnet.

☐ A current-carrying wire will not experience a force if it is at an angle of
45° to the magnetic field of a permanent magnet.

Q4 The diagram shows an aerial view of a copper wire carrying a current down into the page.

Electrical wire with
insulated copper core

N ⊗ S

State which way the wire will move.

....

The Simple Electric Motor

Q1 Which of the following will **not** make an electric motor spin faster? Tick **one** of the boxes.

☐   Using a stronger magnetic field.

☐   Using a bigger current.

☐   Using a commutator.

Q2 Read the three statements below. Tick the box next to each statement that you think is **true**.

☐   The split-ring commutator increases the size of the electric current.

☐   The split-ring commutator reverses the direction of the current every half turn by swapping the contacts to the DC supply.

☐   The split-ring commutator makes the motor rotate in a different direction.

Q3 Suggest two ways in which the direction of spin of a simple DC motor can be reversed.

....

....

Q4 The electric motor is often used in lifts in tall buildings and mines.
Describe briefly how an electric motor can be used to raise (and lower) a lift cage.

....

....

....

Q5 Fill in the blanks, using the words below, to explain how a **loudspeaker** works. Use the **diagram** of a loudspeaker to the right to help you.

move	amplifier	force	field
sound	magnetic	frequency	current

The loudspeaker relies on the fact that a wire carrying a .... in a

.... can experience a .... A coil is attached

to a cardboard or plastic cone. An AC signal is then sent to the coil from an ....

This makes the coil .... and causes the cone to vibrate. The cone vibrates at the

same .... as the signal from the amplifier and produces ....

Electromagnetic Induction

Q1 The apparatus in the diagram below can be used to demonstrate electromagnetic induction.

Centre-reading ammeter

N S

Electrical wire

a) What is electromagnetic induction?

....

....

....

b) Describe how you could use the apparatus to demonstrate electromagnetic induction.

....

....

c) What would you see on the ammeter?

....

d) What effect would swapping the magnets have?

....

Q2 Moving a magnet inside an electric coil produces a trace on a cathode ray oscilloscope.

When the magnet was pushed **inside** the coil, **trace A** was produced on the screen.

a) Explain how trace B could be produced.

....

....

b) Explain how trace C could be produced.

....

c) Explain how trace D could be produced.

....

Coil

N S

Bar magnet

Cathode ray oscilloscope

Traces on oscilloscope

A   B   C   D

Q3 To the right is a diagram of a **dynamo** used to power lights on a bicycle. Use the diagram to help you explain **how** a dynamo works.

....

....

....

....

cog wheel

magnet

coil of wire on soft iron core

wheel

wires to light

Transformers

Q1 The sentences below describe how a **transformer** works but are in the wrong order. Number the boxes 1 to 5 to show the correct order.

☐ The magnetic field produced inside the secondary coil induces an alternating potential difference at the ends of the secondary coil.

☐ This produces an alternating magnetic field in the iron core.

☐ An alternating current flows in the primary coil.

☐ If this is applied to an external circuit, an alternating current will flow in that circuit.

☐ A source of alternating potential difference is applied to the primary coil.

Q2 Look at the diagram to the right showing two electrical circuits.

When the switch is closed, a deflection is seen on the ammeter and then the needle returns to zero. When the switch is opened again, a deflection is seen in the opposite direction.

a) Explain why this happens.

....

....

....

b) What could you add to the apparatus to make the needle move further?

....

Q3 Tick the boxes to indicate whether the following statements are **true** or **false**.

True False

Step-down transformers have fewer turns on the secondary coil than the primary coil. ☐ ☐

If you put a DC into the primary coil, a DC will be produced in the secondary coil. ☐ ☐

When a transformer is operating it behaves as though a bar magnet was being pushed into and pulled out of the secondary coil. ☐ ☐

Q4 Many household electrical goods such as computers and radios need a lower voltage than the 230 V mains voltage. What sort of transformer is used to reduce the voltage for these goods?

....

Top Tips: It can be a bit tricky remembering how a transformer works — make sure you can describe **how** a potential difference is induced in the **secondary coil**. Not only will it be useful in case a question pops up on the exam, but it's also a great icebreaker topic when meeting new people.

Transformers

Q5   The following statements are **false**. Below each statement, write a correct version.

a)   A transformer consists of an iron core and one wire coil.

....

b)   Step-up transformers have more turns on the primary coil than the secondary coil.

....

....

c)   In a step-down transformer the potential difference across the secondary coil is greater than the potential difference across the primary coil.

....

....

....

Derek's transformation didn't go quite as he'd planned.

Q6   Transformers have an **iron core**.

a)   Explain why a potential difference is induced in the **secondary coil** when an alternating current flows in the primary coil.

....

....

b)   Why do transformers work with **alternating** current **only**?

....

....

Q7   Ash is discussing transformers with his friends. He says:

"The core of a transformer has to be made of a conducting material such as iron so the current can get through."

Is Ash right or wrong? Give a reason for your answer.

Ash is .... because ....

....

Transformers

Q8 Many modern appliances use **switch mode transformers**.

a) Tick the boxes to show whether the following statements
about switch mode transformers are **true** or **false**.

	True	False
They usually operate at a frequency between 50 kHz and 200 kHz.	☐	☐
They're usually smaller and lighter than traditional transformers.	☐	☐
They operate at lower frequencies than traditional transformers.	☐	☐
They use very little power when they're switched on and no load is applied.	☐	☐

b) Name **one** device that uses a switch mode transformer.

....

Q9 Tim is investigating a transformer. He uses it to power a **spotlight**, and measures
the **voltage** and **current** for both the **primary** and **secondary coils**. Here are his results.

Voltage to primary coil (V)	Current in primary coil (A)	Voltage to secondary coil (V)	Current in secondary coil (A)
240	0.25	12	5.0

a) Is Tim's transformer a **step-up** or **step-down** transformer? Give a reason for your answer.

....

....

b) i) Calculate the power in the **primary** coil when using the spotlight.

....

....

ii) Calculate the power in the **secondary** coil when using the spotlight.

....

....

c) What idea about the **efficiency** of a transformer is confirmed by Tim's results?

....

Top Tips: Crikey, you should know transformers inside and out after all those wonderful
questions... and there's another juicy page of questions still to come. Make sure you can rearrange
the transformer equations with ease and know the advantages of switch mode transformers too.

Transformers

Q10 A transformer has 100 turns in its primary coil and 4000 turns in its secondary coil. What input voltage would produce an output voltage of 10 000 V?

....

....

Q11 Use the **transformer equation** to complete the following table.

Number of turns on primary coil	Voltage to primary coil (V)	Number of turns on secondary coil	Voltage to secondary coil (V)
1000	12	4000	
1000		2000	20
1000	12		12
	33 000	500	230

Q12 A transformer has **5000** turns on its **primary** coil and **8000** turns on its **secondary** coil.

a) If the input voltage is 230 V, find the output voltage.

....

b) Andy has built a radio which needs a 20 V electricity supply. The mains supply to Andy's house is 230 V. How could Andy adapt the transformer described above to make it suitable for his radio?

....

....

....

....

Q13 A transformer in an adaptor is used to **step down** a **230 V** mains electricity supply to the **110 V** needed for an electric fan heater.

Calculate the current drawn by the transformer from the mains supply, if the current through the heater is **20 A**. Assume that the transformer is 100% efficient.

....

....

<u>Mixed Questions — Physics 3b</u>

Q1   Point P marks the pivot point on the wheelbarrow.

a)   Take moments about P to find the **vertical** force, F, that needs to be applied to the handles of the wheelbarrow to just lift it off the ground.

....

....

b)   The wheelbarrow tipped over while it was being pushed, fully loaded, across some rocky ground. Explain why this happened using the phrases **resultant moment** and **centre of mass** in your answer.

....

....

c)   Write down **two** factors which affect the stability of an object.

1. ....

2. ....

Q2   Mick takes his younger brother Huck on a trip to a fairground.

a)   They decide to go on the swinging pirate ship first. If the time period of each swing of the ship is **2 seconds**, calculate the **frequency** of the ship.

....

b)   Mick wins a goldfish on a fairground stall. When he squeezes the top of bag, water squirts out of a hole at the bottom. Explain briefly, in terms of **forces**, why this happens.

....

....

c)   Mick decides to try out the "Test Your Strength!" game.

The game works using a **simple hydraulic system** (see right). Mick uses a wooden mallet to hit a small piston.

Use the diagram to explain why the **upwards** force at the larger piston will be **greater** than the force of the mallet on the smaller piston.

....

....

....

Physics 3b — Forces and Electromagnetism

Mixed Questions — Physics 3b

Q3   The diagram below shows how an **electromagnet** can be used to switch on a car's starter motor.

a)   What is the function of the iron core, C?

....

....

b)   Describe what happens when the switch, S, is closed.

....

....

....

....

Q4   The diagram below shows a simple **motor**. The coil is rotating as shown.

a)   On the diagram, draw arrows labelled 'F' to show the direction of the **force** on each arm of the coil.

b)   Draw arrows labelled 'I' on each arm of the coil to show the direction the **current** is flowing.

c)   State two ways of increasing the **speed** of this motor.

1..

2..

Q5   The diagram shows a **bicycle dynamo**.

a)   What happens in the coil of wire when the knob is rotated **clockwise** at a constant speed? Explain your answer.

....

....

....

b)   What would change if the magnet were rotated **anticlockwise** (at the same speed as before)?

....

Mixed Questions — Physics 3b

Q6   TV satellite **A** shown below orbits the Earth at a distance of 35 800 km above the surface.

a)   What provides the centripetal force that keeps the satellite moving in a circular path?

....

b)   Indicate whether each of these statements is true or false.   **True**   **False**

i)   The satellite is moving at a constant velocity.   ☐   ☐

ii) The centripetal force acts away from the centre of the circle.   ☐   ☐

c)   Satellite B has the same mass as satellite A and is in orbit 40 000 km above the Earth.

Which satellite, A or B, has the greatest centripetal force acting on it? ....

Q7   The diagram shows a traditional **transformer**.

a)   What is the output voltage, V?

....

....

....

230 V AC   1000 turns   200 turns   V

b)   Transformers are usually wound on a **core**.

i)   Name the metal used for the core of the transformer. ....

ii) Why is the core a necessary part of a transformer?

....

....

c)   A different transformer is needed to 'step down' a power supply from 33 kV to 230 V.
It has 2000 turns on its primary coil. How many turns should it have on its secondary coil?

....

....

d)   Describe the advantages of using a **switch mode transformer** in a
mobile phone charger, compared to a traditional transformer.

....

....

....

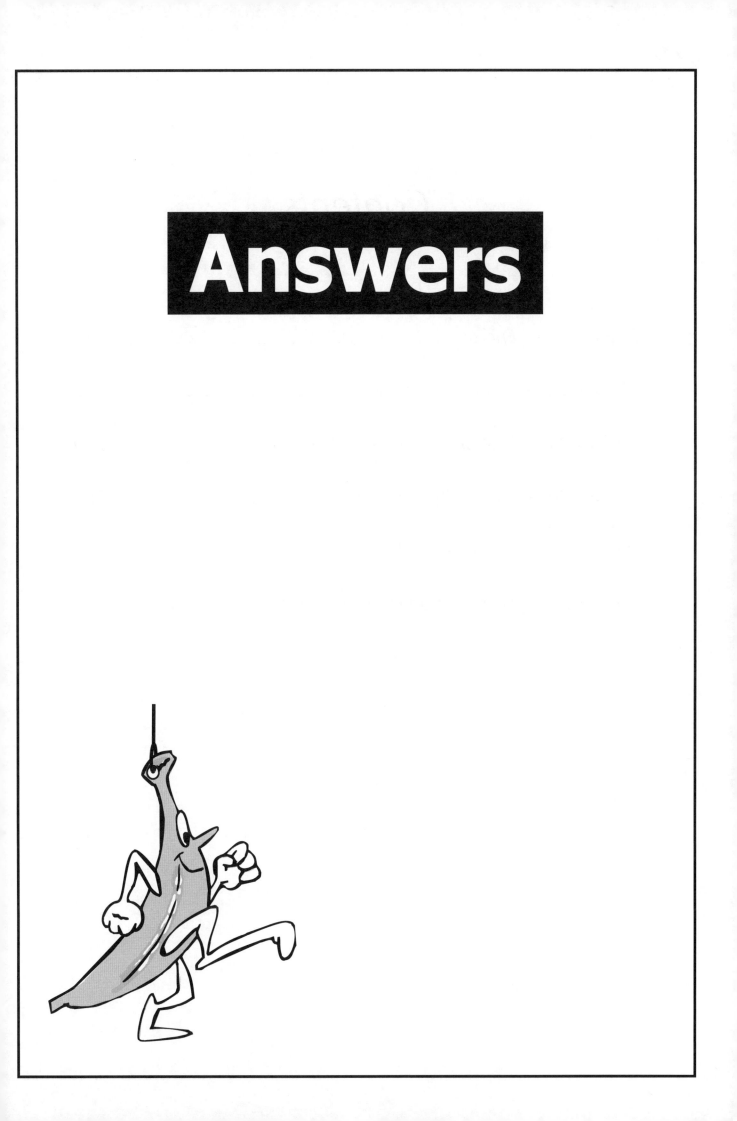

Answers

Contents

Physics 1a — Energy

Physics 1a — Energy

Pages 1-2 — Heat Radiation

Q1 a) i) True
ii) True
iii) False
iv) True
v) False
b) Hot objects do absorb infrared radiation.
Cold objects do emit infrared radiation (but much less than hot objects).

Q2 a) Dark, matt surfaces are **good** absorbers and **good** emitters of infrared radiation.
b) The best surfaces for radiating infrared are **good** absorbers and **good** emitters.
c) Silvered surfaces are **poor** absorbers and **poor** emitters of infrared radiation.
d) The best surfaces for solar hot water panels are **good** absorbers and **good** emitters.

Q3 a) Infrared radiation is emitted from the **surface** of hot solid objects **and** from liquids and gases.
b) **All** objects absorb infrared radiation — the bigger the difference in temperature between an object and its surroundings, the **faster** the rate of heat transfer.

Q4 So they lose as little heat energy as possible by radiation (shiny surfaces are poor emitters).

Q5 a) False
b) True
c) True
d) False
e) True

Q6 Flask B will cool fastest because there is a larger temperature difference between the water and the air in the box.

Q7 E.g. Paint the radiator matt black. Put a shiny inner surface between the radiator and the roof. Put a glass (or similar) sheet in front of it. Use a different material for the radiator. Use a bigger radiator. Tilt the radiator so it faces straight at the Sun at noon.

Page 3 — Kinetic Theory

Q1

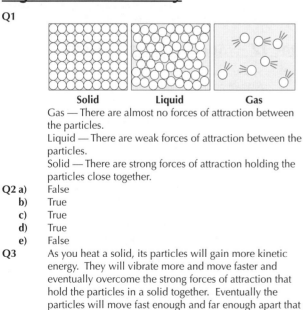

Solid **Liquid** **Gas**

Gas — There are almost no forces of attraction between the particles.
Liquid — There are weak forces of attraction between the particles.
Solid — There are strong forces of attraction holding the particles close together.

Q2 a) False
b) True
c) True
d) True
e) False

Q3 As you heat a solid, its particles will gain more kinetic energy. They will vibrate more and move faster and eventually overcome the strong forces of attraction that hold the particles in a solid together. Eventually the particles will move fast enough and far enough apart that the substance will become a liquid.

Page 4 — Conduction

Q1 a) True
b) False
c) True
d) True

Q2 The piece of wood feels quite warm because wood is a poor conductor, so it does not conduct much heat energy away from George's hand. The metal spoon feels colder because metal is a good conductor, so it conducts heat energy away from his hand very quickly.

Q3 a) Insulator
b) Conductor
c) Conductor
d) Conductor

Q4 a) Copper is a good conductor because it's got free electrons in it. All materials contain electrons, but if they're not free electrons they don't help conduction.
b) Colour and shininess don't make any difference to conduction. Mamphela is getting mixed up with radiation, where it does make a difference.
c) All the particles in all materials have kinetic energy. Ruth doesn't explain that the free electrons mean that kinetic energy is able to move about so easily in copper.

Pages 5-6 — Convection

Q1 a) i) True
ii) False
iii) True
iv) False
b) ii) The colder the water, the denser it is. (Note: this is only true above 4 °C. Below 4 °C, water gets less dense as it cools.)
iv) Convection currents can happen in any liquid or gas.

Q2 The very bottom of a hot water tank stays cold... because water doesn't conduct much heat.
Warm air rises... because it is not so dense.
A small heater can send heat all over a room... because heat flows from warm places to cooler ones.

Q3 a) The particles gain more energy as heat is transferred from the radiator to the air.
b) The particles have more energy so move around faster. The distance between them becomes greater, so the air expands and becomes less dense. This reduction in density means the hotter air rises above the cooler, denser air.

Q4 a)

b) The water is heated by conduction.
The temperature of the water increases.
The water expands (as its temperature increases).
The water becomes less dense (as it expands as the particles get further apart).
The warm water floats upwards and is replaced by denser cold water from the right.

Q5 The experiment shows that convection works very well in water — the ice melts because convection currents carry warm water upwards. It also shows that water is a poor **conductor** of heat — convection currents do not warm the water below the flame, and the water below the heater stays cold because conduction only occurs very slowly.

Physics 1a — Energy

Page 7 — Condensation and Evaporation

Q1 liquid, cools, kinetic energy, attractive.

Q2 a) i) True

   ii) False

   iii) False

   b) ii) Particles can evaporate from a liquid at temperatures much lower than the liquid's boiling point.

   iii) The speed of a particle, its mass, the direction it's travelling in and how near the surface it is all affect whether it can escape a liquid.

Q3 Sweating cools you down — when the sweat on your skin evaporates it causes a cooling effect. This is because the fastest particles (the ones with most kinetic energy) are most likely to evaporate from a liquid (the sweat). When they do, the average speed and kinetic energy of the remaining particles decreases. This decrease in average particle energy means the temperature of the remaining liquid falls. Sweating more will increase this cooling effect, as more particles will evaporate from skin.

Q4 a) E.g. if the liquid has a high temperature, low density, large surface area and if there is a low concentration of the liquid in the air it's evaporating into.

   b) E.g. if the temperature of the surface the gas touches is lower, if the surface area of the surface the gas touches is larger.

Pages 8-9 — Rate of Heat Transfer

Q1 a) To maximise the amount of heat transfer.

   b) Metal is a good conductor so it will conduct heat away from the radiator much faster than air, as air is an insulator.

Q2 Any four from:
Shiny surfaces — reduce radiation.
Insulating foam supports — reduce conduction.
Vacuum gap between walls of bottle — reduce conduction and convection.
Stopper made of poor conductors, e.g. plastic — reduces conduction.
Air space between bottle and outer case — reduces conduction.
Outer case made of plastic — reduces conduction.

Q3 E.g.

	Suggested Improvements
Radiation	Make the outside surface shiny / white / silvery.
Conduction	Cover the tank with 'lagging' material that conducts poorly, e.g. fibreglass.
Convection	Have the tank in a cupboard so warm air can't 'escape', or put a loose cover over it.

Q4 a) The hairs 'stand up' to trap a thicker layer of insulating air around your body to limit the amount of heat lost by convection.

   b) Their skin goes pink as the body diverts more blood to flow near the surface of the skin so that more heat can be lost by radiation.

Q5 a) i) Fox A — desert.

   ii) Fox B — Arctic.

   b) Large ears give a large surface area for Fox A to lose heat from easily by radiation. This helps Fox A avoid overheating in a hot climate. Fox B's small ears give a small surface area to minimise heat loss by radiation and stay warm in a cold climate.

Q6 a) Reading down the table: 3 : 1, 1.5 : 1, 1 : 1, 0.75 : 1, 0.6 : 1.

   b) The surface area : volume ratio decreases as the size of the cube increases.

   c) The small cube, because it has a small volume where it can hold heat but a relatively large surface over which it can lose it.

d) Fins increase the surface area of the car engine so it has a larger surface area to volume ratio. This means heat will be radiated away quicker so the engine cools quicker.

Pages 10-11 — Energy Efficiency in the Home

Q1 a) Through the roof — loft insulation.
Through the walls — cavity wall insulation.
Through the doors — double glazing of any glass panels, draught-proofing strips around the frames and letter box.

   b) She could install double glazing, fit draught-proofing strips around the windows, and have thick curtains. (Or she could turn her heating down.)

Q2 a) Cavity wall insulation — reduces heat transfer by convection, because pockets of air are trapped in the foam, and can't move between the two walls. The foam and the air trapped in it are both insulators, so heat transfer by conduction is reduced. It also reduces radiation across the gap.

   b) Loft insulation — layers of fibreglass wool reduce heat transfer by conduction from the ceiling to the roof space. Heat transfer by radiation is reduced, because the loft floor is not so warm.

Q3 a) Payback time = 1200 ÷ 20 = 60 years.

   b) No, because although the shutters are cheaper, they are less cost-effective — they have a longer payback time.

Q4 a) U-values measure how effective a material is as an insulator.

   b) Gary should choose brand A because it has a lower U-value — the lower the U-value, the better the material is as an insulator, so heat transfer will be less.

Q5 a) Shona is right — a method that pays for itself faster will start saving you money sooner.
Alison is right — good value means getting a good effect from the money spent.
Tim is wrong — cheap or badly installed insulation might not work very well.
Meena is wrong — cost-effectiveness means getting a good energy saving per pound spent.

   b) If you plan to move house soon, it makes sense to choose a method with a short payback time. But if you stay in the house for 20 years, say, you would save more in the long term by choosing a method which might cost more to install but gave higher annual savings.

Page 12 — Specific Heat Capacity

Q1 a) Specific heat capacity is the amount of energy needed to raise the temperature of 1 kg of a substance by 1 °C.

   b) Substance A

Q2 a) Concrete

   b) Water is used because it has a really high specific heat capacity so it can store large amounts of heat, and can be easily pumped around pipes.

Q3 Energy = Mass × SHC × temperature change.
The temperature change for both is 50 °C.
Energy from mercury = 27.2 × 139 × 50 = 189 040 J.
Energy from water = 2 × 4200 × 50 = 420 000 J.
Difference = 420 000 − 189 040 = **230 960 J** (≈ 231 kJ).

Q4 Rearrange the energy equation:
Mass = Energy ÷ (SHC × temperature change).
Mass = 3040 ÷ (380 × 40) = 3040 ÷ 15 200
= **0.2 kg** of copper (or **200 g**).

Pages 13-14 — Energy Transfer

Q1 conservation, transferred, dissipated, created.

Q2 a) **chemical energy** → heat and light energy.

   b) electrical energy → **sound and heat energy.**

   c) **electrical energy** → **light and heat energy.**

Physics 1a — Energy

Q3 a) i) chemical energy
ii) heat/thermal energy (and kinetic energy)
b) Any two from:
Chemical energy → heat energy (as the coal burns).
Heat energy → kinetic energy (as the steam drives the engine).
Chemical energy → light energy (in the lamp).
Other answers are possible.

Q4 a) Gravitational potential energy.
b) Chemical energy from the porridge is transferred to kinetic energy in Bruce's muscles and the moving bar. This kinetic energy is then transferred to gravitational potential energy.
c) The gravitational potential energy is transferred into kinetic energy as it falls downwards.

Q5 Electric fan — kinetic energy
Iron — heat energy
Bedside table lamp — light energy

Q6 1. Chemical energy from the archer's food is stored in his muscles.
2. Chemical energy in the archer's muscles is transferred into elastic potential energy.
3. Energy stored in the pulled bow and string is transferred into kinetic energy.
4. As it goes upwards the arrow loses kinetic energy and gains gravitational potential energy.
5. The arrow loses gravitational potential energy and gains kinetic energy as it falls to earth.

Q7 a) In a battery-powered torch, the battery transfers **chemical** energy into **electrical** energy OR the **bulb** transfers electrical energy into light energy.
b) A wind turbine transfers kinetic energy into electrical energy **and heat and sound energy**.
c) A wind-up toy car transfers **elastic potential energy** into kinetic energy and sound energy.

Q8 a) E.g. loudspeaker or buzzer/bell.
b) Solar cell/photovoltaic cell.
c) E.g. hair dryer or electric fan heater.

Pages 15-17 — Efficiency of Machines

Q1 transfer, useful, heat, fraction, input, output.
Q2 a) 100 J
b) 5 J
c) 95 J
Q3

	Total Energy Input (J)	Useful Energy Output (J)	Efficiency
1	2000	1500	**0.75 (or 75%)**
2	**4000**	2000	0.50
3	4000	**1000**	0.25

Q4 Useful power output = efficiency × total power input
= 0.9 × 2000 = 1800 W.

Q5 The winch, like all other devices, is not 100% efficient. 10 J of the 20 J of input energy was 'wasted'. Much of this waste was likely to have been heat energy, generated by friction and electrical resistance in the motor, and between the moving parts of the winch.

Q6 a) By seeing how long each MP3 player can run before the batteries run out. Comparing the times is equivalent to comparing the useful energy outputs (the useful energy output will be proportional to the time).
b) Any two from:
Play the same music, play (the same) music at the same volume, use the same number/type of batteries.
c) Player B is more efficient than player A. In fact player B is one-third more efficient than player A (or player A is only three-quarters as efficient as B).

Q7 A heat exchanger can be used to transfer some of the

waste heat energy from the car's engine to the air that's used to warm the passenger compartment.

Q8 a) Any two from:
Longer life.
Cheaper to run OR uses less energy/electricity.
Cheaper to buy per year of its lifetime.
(Or other sensible answers.)
b) Any two from:
Cheaper to buy.
Bright as soon as you switch it on.
Low-energy bulbs can't be used with dimmer switches.
(Or other sensible answers.)

Pages 18-19 — Energy Transformation Diagrams

Q1 a) 10 J.
b) 150 J.
Q2 See diagram below — where the scale is 1 small square = 2 J. Different scales are possible.

Q3 1. The input energy is not shown clearly. The 100 J kinetic energy should be shown as input energy.
2. The quantities of energy do not add up. The electrical energy plus the waste heat energy should equal the input energy. Either the input should be 175 J, or the heat wasted should be 25 J. (Or all the values are wrong).

Q4 a) 100 J heat + 40 J GPE = 140 J
b) 60 J
c) Efficiency = 60 ÷ 200 = 0.3.

Pages 20-21 — The Cost of Electricity

Q1 a) Energy used = 2 kW × 3 hours = **6 kWh**.
b) Cost of energy = 14p/kWh × 6 kWh = **84p**.
Q2 Energy used = 0.1 kW × 10 h = 1 kWh, so the cost is **11.3p**.
Q3 A 60 W lamp on for 9 h uses 0.06 × 9 = **0.54 kWh**.
An 8 kW shower on for 0.25 h uses 8 × 0.25 = **2 kWh**.
So Tina is right — the shower uses nearly four times as much energy as the lamp.
Q4 a) 34783 – 34259 = **524 kWh**.
b) 524 × 9.7p = 5083p (to nearest penny) = **£50.83**.
Q5 a) Number of kWh used = 7 × 275 × 1000
= 1 925 000 kWh so cost = kWh × night time cost per kWh
= 1 925 000 × 3.7 = 7 122 500p or **£71 225**.
b) kWh generated = 5 × 288 × 1000 = 1 440 000 kWh so cost = kWh × daytime cost per kWh
= 1 440 000 × 7.2 = 10 368 000 or **£103 680**.
Q6 Difference between meter readings on first night
= 13598.63 – 13592.42 = 6.21 kWh
Difference between meter readings on second night
= 13649.41 – 13646.68 = 2.73 kWh
Difference between energy usage on 1st and 2nd night
= 6.21 – 2.73 = **3.48 kWh**.

Physics 1b — Electricity and Waves

Page 22 — Choosing Electrical Appliances

Q1   E.g. It can be used in locations where there is no access to mains electricity. / It's easier to use as there is no power cord to get in the way/restrict movement.

Q2 a)   Battery powered lamp: Energy used to fully charge (enough for 8 hours use) = 400 W × 6 hours = 2.4 kWh
Mains powered lamp: Energy used in 8 hours = 1.6 kW × 8 = 12.8 kWh
So, difference in energy used = 12.8 − 2.4 = **10.4 kWh**

b)   Difference in cost = 10.4 × 12 = **124.8p**

c)   E.g. There might not be an electricity supply where they are camping, so they will not be able to use a mains powered lamp or recharge the battery powered lamp when it runs out. The wind up lamp does not require any electricity to recharge.

Q3   E.g. any two from: can be used to power X-ray machines / refrigeration of medicines/vaccines / can power lighting/ equipment for operations / refrigeration of food.

Pages 23-25 — Mixed Questions — Physics 1a

Q1 a)   Pockets of air are trapped in bubbles of foam, reducing convection and radiation across the gap. Air is an insulator, so it also reduces conduction.

b)   Paul should look for a low U-value because materials with a low U-value are better insulators, so heat loss will be less.

c)   The condensation happens because water vapour in the air cools as it comes into contact with the cold surface. As the vapour cools, the particles in it slow down and lose kinetic energy. The particles no longer have enough kinetic energy to overcome the attractive forces between them, so the vapour becomes a liquid.

Q2 a)   E.g.

b)   The matt black surface is a better absorber of heat radiation (from the Bunsen burner flame) than the shiny silver surface. The matt black surface is also a better emitter of radiation, so the temperature rise for A will be quicker/steeper than for B.

c)   chemical energy → heat, light energy and sound energy

Q3 a)   The freezer compartment cools the warmer air at the top of the fridge, which then falls, forcing warmer air to rise.

b)   Energy (in kWh) = Power (in kW) × Time (in h)
= 0.5 kW × 24 h = 12 kWh.
Cost = No. of units × price per unit
= 12 kWh × 15p = **180p** (= £1.80)

Q4 a)   Hot water tank jacket.

b)   Over 5 years, the savings would be:
Hot water tank jacket: (5 × £15) − £15 = £60
Draught-proofing: (5 × £65) − £70 = £255
Cavity wall insulation: (5 × £70) − £560 = −£210
Thermostatic controls: (5 × £25) − £120 = £5.
So **draught-proofing** would save the most money.

c)   The temperature change required is 36 − 14 = 22 °C.
Energy = mass × SHC × change in temperature
= 90 × 4200 × 22 = **8 316 000 J** (= 8316 kJ = 8.316 MJ).

Q5 a)   Chemical energy.

b)   E.g. below, using a scale of 1 small square = 25 joules. Other scales are possible.

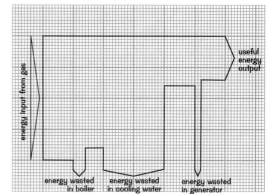

c)   Useful output energy = 1000 J − 100 J − 500 J − 50 J = 350 J.
So efficiency = 350 ÷ 1000 = **0.35** (or 35%).

Q6 a)   Fins increase the surface area of the heat sink — a larger surface area means they emit heat quickly.

b) i)   Metals are good conductors of heat because they have free electrons which can quickly transfer energy.

ii)   The free electrons at the hot end move faster and collide with other free electrons, transferring energy. These other electrons then pass on their extra energy to other electrons, and so on across the piece of metal.

Physics 1b — Electricity and Waves

Page 26 — Energy Sources & Power Stations

Q1   1. Coal is burned to release heat.
2. Water is heated in a boiler and turned to steam.
3. Hot steam rushes through a turbine and makes it spin.
4. The spinning turbine makes the generator spin too.
5. Electricity is produced by the spinning generator.

Q2 a)   Nuclear fission produces heat.

b)   Non-renewable sources will eventually run out / cannot be replaced when they are used up.

Q3   Most power stations use **non-renewable** sources of energy, such as coal, oil or gas. These **fossil** fuels are initially burnt in a boiler. This converts the **chemical** energy in the fuel to **heat** energy. A turbine then converts this energy into **kinetic** energy, which, in turn is converted to **electrical** energy by a generator. This energy feeds into the national grid ready to be distributed to consumers.

Q4   Wind and solar power are unreliable as they depend on appropriate weather conditions to generate power. Whereas fossil fuels can be burnt all the time.

Page 27 — Renewable Energy Sources (1)

Q1 a)   Any three from: they make a lot of noise, they spoil the view/landscape / cause visual pollution, they harm wildlife / they kill birds, they only work if it's windy, the electricity they generate is expensive, a lot of turbines are needed to replace one power station.

b)   Any three from: once running, there's no permanent damage to the landscape, they use a renewable, free source of energy, running costs are low, they don't release greenhouse gases into the atmosphere.

Q2   Disadvantages — the initial costs are high, and most solar cells are not very efficient, they don't work well when it's cloudy. Advantages — they use a renewable and free source of energy (there are no fuel costs), they are a good way to provide energy in remote places, there is no pollution when they are in use.

Physics 1b — Electricity and Waves

Q3 a) They're a good source of energy in situations where only a small amount of electricity is needed, e.g. calculators. They're often available in places where there is no access to mains electricity, e.g. remote road signs.

b) The cost of connecting the remote farm to the National Grid would be enormous compared with the value of the electricity generated.

Pages 28-29 — Renewable Energy Sources (2)

Q1 a) Measurements provide more information than observations. The voltage gives a more accurate idea of how much energy was transferred.

b) Their results **do not support** their prediction because the relationship is not proportional — e.g. halving the height (200 cm to 100 cm) does not halve the voltage (0.2 V is not half of 1.1 V).

Q2 1. At night big power stations make more electricity than is needed.
2. Spare electricity is used to pump water from reservoirs at a low level to others at a high level.
3. Water at a high level stores energy until it is needed.
4. At peak times, when demand is the highest, water is allowed to flow downhill, powering turbines and generating electricity.

Q3 Big coal-fired power stations deliver energy... all the time.
Pumped storage power stations deliver energy... that they have previously stored / when it is needed.
Hydroelectric power stations deliver electricity... when it is needed.

Q4 a) The student could say that no atmospheric pollution is produced when electricity is being generated, or that building the dams and manufacturing the turbines, generators etc. does cause atmospheric pollution/or that the power plant will cause both visual and noise pollution.

b) The student could say that there are no fuel costs, or that building dams and purchasing turbines etc. is expensive.

c) The student might argue that dams are unsightly, they disturb the natural environment, and disrupt / destroy wildlife habitats etc., or they could argue that an impressive engineering structure has a positive visual impact, and/or that not all hydroelectric projects involve building dams.

d) The student could say that it is rare for reservoirs to be empty even in dry weather, and water can be released to power the generators when it's needed most, or they could say that power supplies are less reliable during droughts, and this may be a more serious problem in the future.

e) Any two from: it is a renewable source of energy, it does not contribute to global warming (once running), the output can be varied more quickly than that of most other power stations, good for use in remote locations.

f) Any two from: rotting vegetation releases greenhouse gases (methane and CO_2) when the valley is flooded, set-up costs are high, set-up times are long, destruction of wildlife habitats.

Page 30 — Renewable Energy Sources (3)

Q1 a) Tidal.
b) Wave.
c) Tidal.
d) Wave.
e) Tidal.

Q2 a) When the tide comes in the water passes through the turbines and then builds up behind the barrage. When the tide goes out the water is allowed out through the turbines in the barrage at a controlled speed. As the water passes through the turbines electricity is generated. (The water also turns the turbines on the way in.)

b) Any two from the following: Initial costs are fairly high. Barrages can look unattractive. Barrages can prevent access for boats. Barrages can damage habitats. The height of tides is variable. No energy is available at the turn of the tides.

Q3 a) 1. A wave moves water upwards, forcing air out towards a turbine.
2. The moving air makes the turbine spin.
3. The spinning turbine drives a generator.
4. The spinning generator makes electricity.
5. The water goes down again.
6. Air is sucked downwards, spinning the turbine the other way and generating more power.

b) Any two from the following: High initial costs. Spoiling the view. Can be unreliable because it depends on winds. It is currently only suitable for small-scale use. Can be a hazard to boats.

Page 31 — Renewable Energy Sources (4)

Q1 Biofuels are used to generate electricity in a similar way to **fossil fuels**. Biofuels are burnt to heat **water** and make **steam**, which is used to drive **turbines** to power generators and make electricity.
Biofuels can be solids (e.g. **woodchips**), liquids (e.g. **ethanol**) or gases (e.g. **methane**).

Q2 In some volcanic areas, hot water and steam rise to the surface. This steam can be used to drive turbines to generate electricity.

Q3 Biofuels will not run out — more can always be made to us as a source of energy.

Q4 a) False
b) False
c) False
d) True

Page 32 — Energy Sources and the Environment

Q1 Acid rain... sulfur dioxide formed by burning oil and coal.
Climate change... releasing CO_2 by burning fossil fuels.
Dangerous radioactive waste... using nuclear power.
Spoiling of natural landscapes... coal mining OR sulfur dioxide formed by burning oil and coal.

Q2 Answer will depend on student's opinion but should include an explanation of their reasoning, e.g. Lisa because nuclear power produces long-lasting, dangerous, radioactive waste. Or Ben because nuclear power is carefully controlled to reduce any dangers. Also, nuclear power doesn't produce any carbon dioxide, whereas using fossil fuels adds to the carbon dioxide in the atmosphere, leading to climate change / an increased greenhouse effect / global warming.

Q3 Plants that are used to produce biofuels (or to feed animals that produce biofuels) absorb carbon dioxide from the atmosphere. Burning the biofuel puts the carbon back into the atmosphere as carbon dioxide, so overall there is a neutral effect on the atmosphere.

Q4 a) This is the process of collecting carbon dioxide from power stations before it is released into the atmosphere.

b) E.g. in empty gas fields, oil fields, dissolved in seawater at the bottom of the ocean, capturing with algae.

Pages 33-34 — Comparison of Energy Resources

Q1 Gas

Q2 a) Any one of: gas supplies often need to be imported and there may be steep price rises, gas will run out eventually, burning gas causes atmospheric pollution and contributes to the global warming. Other answers are possible.

Physics 1b — Electricity and Waves

b) Any one of: high set-up costs, high maintenance and/
or decommissioning costs, long set-up times, dangerous
radioactive waste, risk of catastrophic accidents, threat
from terrorism, nuclear fuels need to be imported.
Other answers are possible.

c) Any one of: it's dependent on the weather / only works
when the wind is blowing, unreliable, visual pollution /
spoils the view, noise pollution. Other answers are possible.

d) E.g. high set-up costs. Other answers are possible.

Q3 a) Most (about 75%) of the UK's electricity generation
depends on supplies of coal, oil and gas. These fuels are
all non-renewable and will run out eventually.

b) 1. We don't know how to dispose of the radioactive waste
safely.
2. Nuclear power stations and radioactive waste are targets
for terrorists.

c) Shutting down / removing from active status.

d) Answer will depend on student's opinion. 'I agree' could
be backed up by mentioning that sea levels change in a
predictable and reliable way, twice every day, and/or that
the UK has a long coastline and plenty of opportunities
to use the resource. 'I disagree' could be backed up by
saying that there are only a few suitable estuaries, or that
at neap tides, the difference in sea level between low and
high tides is small, so there is not much energy available.

e) E.g. Any two from: it's a reliable source of energy, it
doesn't release greenhouse gases, we're not likely to run
out of uranium any time soon (and some of the waste can
be reprocessed and reused).

Pages 35-36 — Electricity and the National Grid

Q1 1. Electrical energy is generated in power stations.
2. The voltage of the supply is raised.
3. An electrical current flows through power cables across
the country.
4. The voltage of the supply is reduced.
5. Mrs Miggins boils the kettle for tea.

Q2 a) Underground cables
b) Overhead cables
c) Overhead cables
d) Overhead cables
e) Underground cables
f) Overhead cables
g) Underground cables

Q3 a) Step-up transformer, pylons, step-down transformer,
insulators.

b) At higher voltages, less energy is wasted as heat. This
saves more money than the cost of the equipment.

Q4 a) The National Grid transmits energy at high voltage and
low current.

b) A step-up transformer is used to **increase** the voltage of
the supply (OR reduce the **current**) before electricity is
transmitted.

c) Using a **low current** (OR high **voltage**) makes sure there is
not much energy wasted.

Q5 a) Supply is the amount of electricity generated and delivered
to consumers. Demand is the amount of electricity
needed by the consumers.

b) Consumer demand for energy is increasing, so the National
Grid has to increase the supply to meet this demand.

c) E.g. More plants can be built, power output of power
plants can be increased.

d) E.g. Use energy efficient appliances, being more careful
not to waste energy in the home (e.g. by turning off lights).

Pages 37-38 — Wave Basics

Q1 energy, matter
Q2 a) Transverse — 2, Longitudinal — 1.

b) E.g. transverse waves can travel in a vacuum but
longitudinal waves cannot / vibrations in a transverse
wave are perpendicular to the direction of energy transfer,
whereas in longitudinal waves they are parallel to the
direction of energy transfer.

Q3 a) A and C
b) A and B
c) A and C

Q4 Transverse
vibrations are at 90° to the direction of energy transfer
produced by a slinky spring whose end is wiggled at 90° to
the spring itself
ripples on water
electromagnetic radiation
Longitudinal
vibrations are along the same direction as the energy
transfer
sound waves
produced by a slinky spring whose end is pushed and
pulled towards and away from the rest of the spring

Q5 a) metres
b) There are 25 waves per second.
c) A

Q6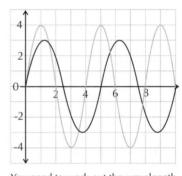

Q7 You need to work out the frequency.
Using $v = f\lambda$ and rearranging gives
frequency = speed ÷ wavelength.
So frequency = $(3 \times 10^8) \div (5 \times 10^{-7}) = \mathbf{6 \times 10^{14}\,Hz}$.

Q8 a) He has drawn a wave with a wavelength of 4 m rather than
2 m.

b)

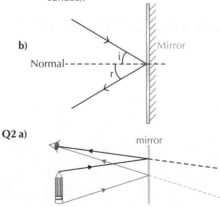

Q9 You need to work out the wavelength.
Using $v = f\lambda$ and rearranging gives:
wavelength = speed ÷ frequency.
So wavelength = $(3 \times 10^8) \div (4.6 \times 10^{15}) = \mathbf{6.5 \times 10^{-8}\,m}$

Page 39 — Wave Properties

Q1 a) The normal is an imaginary line that's at right angles to the
surface at the point of incidence (where the light hits the
surface).

b)

Q2 a)

Physics 1b — Electricity and Waves

b) virtual
c) upright
d) The left and right hand side of the object are swapped round in the image. E.g. the right hand side of the actual pencil appears to be the left hand side of the pencil on the image.

Page 40 — Refraction and Diffraction

Q1 a) Diffraction is the spreading out of waves when they pass through a gap or past an obstacle.

b)

Q2 a) B
b) Waves don't refract when they're travelling along the normal.
c) When a wave changes direction as it hits the boundary between two different media.
Q3 The gap is too wide. The gap needs to be of similar magnitude (size) to the wavelength of the wave.

Pages 41-42 — EM Waves and Communication

Q1 a)

Radio waves	Micro- waves	Infrared		Ultraviolet	X-rays	Gamma rays
1m-10⁴m	10⁻²m (1 cm)	10⁻⁵m (0.01mm)	10⁻⁷m	10⁻⁸m	10⁻¹⁰m	10⁻¹⁵m

b) The energy of the waves **increases** from **left to right** across the table.
Q2 a) i) False
    ii) False
    iii) False
    iv) True
b) i) Visible light travels **at the same speed** in a vacuum **as** both X-rays and radio waves.
    ii) All EM waves transfer **energy** from place to place.
    iii) Radio waves have the **longest** wavelength of all EM waves.
Q3 A, B and C
Q4 EM waves with higher frequencies have **shorter** wavelengths. The **higher** the frequency of an EM wave, the greater the energy of the wave.
Q5 The house can receive **long-wave** signals because they can diffract around the mountain. It also receives **short-wave** signals because they are reflected by the **ionosphere**. However **FM** signals are not received at the house as the transmitter is not in direct line of sight of the house.
Q6 Things they have in common — any two from: they can both travel in a vacuum, they both travel at the speed of light, they both transfer energy.
(Or other sensible answers.)
Ways in which they differ — any two from: they have different wavelengths, they have different frequencies, they have different energies.
(Or other sensible answers.)

Pages 43-44 — EM Waves and Their Uses

Q1 Infrared
Q2 a) This allows the satellite to send signals to (and receive signals from) a large area of the Earth.
b) Radio waves can't pass easily through the earth's watery atmosphere.
c) Microwaves
Q3 a) Visible light or infrared waves.
b) They are reflected down the core of the fibre.
Q4 The microwaves are not absorbed or reflected much by the water molecules in clouds (unlike visible light).

Q5 a) Microwaves
b) Their brain cells may be heated up and damaged.
c) E.g. convenience (e.g. keeping in touch with friends), safety (they feel the positives outweigh the risks). Also many people only use their phones for short periods of time, so they have limited exposure.
Q6 E.g. The lens focuses the light onto a light sensitive film or electronic sensor. The film or sensor then records the image.

Pages 45-46 — Sound Waves

Q1 C, A, D, B.
Q2 vibrate, high, low.
Q3 The bigger the **amplitude** of a sound wave, the **louder** the sound.
Q4 2000
Q5 a) 30 Hz
b) 5 Hz, 630 Hz, 8 kHz, 21 kHz, 400 kHz, 3 MHz
Q6 a) A reflected sound wave.
b) The soft surfaces in her bedroom absorb the sound vibrations better, so less sound is reflected around the room.
c) The echoed sound has to travel further, and so takes longer to reach your ears.
Q7 a) It gets quieter and eventually stops. Because sound is a vibration passed from molecule to molecule, it cannot be transmitted through a vacuum.
b) The foam prevents the sound from being transmitted through the solid surface that the clock is placed on.

Pages 47-48 — The Origin of the Universe

Q1 a) It will sound lower pitched.
b) Doppler effect
c) The wavelength seems to increase.
d) The frequency would seem to have increased.
Q2 As the train leaves, it moves away from Brian's microphone. So the frequency appears to get slightly **lower**. E.g.

Q3 Light from other galaxies is red-shifted — all the frequencies are lower in the spectrum than is the case for other objects nearby. This tells us that the galaxies are moving away from us.   Also, the further away the galaxy, the greater the red-shift. This tells us that more distant galaxies are moving away from us at a faster rate than nearer galaxies.
Q4 a) The universe started as a single point that exploded in the Big Bang and has been expanding ever since.
b) Space itself is expanding.
Q5 a) Low frequency electromagnetic radiation coming from all parts of the universe.
b) Very shortly after the beginning of the universe, the universe was very hot and emitted very high energy, high frequency radiation. As the universe expanded it cooled, and this radiation dropped in frequency and is now detected as the CMBR.
Q6 E.g. Any one from: It can't explain observed acceleration and expansion of the universe. / It doesn't tell you anything about the universe before the Big Bang.

Pages 49-52 — Mixed Questions — Physics 1b

Q1 a) B represents ultraviolet radiation.
The infrared wave has the largest amplitude.
b) B — They are all transverse waves.
D — They all travel at the same speed in space.

Physics 2a — Motion, Energy and Electricity

Q2 a) i) E.g. Solar cells require little maintenance and no fuel, making them suitable for remote locations (where transporting fuel and arranging repairs would be difficult and expensive). Solar power is a renewable source of energy and won't pollute the island.

ii) E.g. The island is likely to be quite windy. Wind turbines are fairly cheap to install. As with solar power, wind power is renewable, doesn't cause pollution and doesn't require fuel.

b) Wave power — around the coastline, biomass — llama poo could be used to produce biofuel for burning. (Hydroelectric power might also be possible, depending on the island's geography and climate.)

Q3 a) Frequency = speed ÷ wavelength = 3×10^8 m/s ÷ 1500 m = **200 000 Hz** (= 200 kHz).

b) Longer waves diffract more around large objects than shorter waves. So the long-wave radio signal diffracts around the mountains and can be received in Mr Potts' holiday cottage. The TV signal is short-wave so it doesn't diffract much and can't be received in his cottage.

Q4 a) E.g. it's clean / fuel is relatively cheap / it's reliable

b) Carbon capture and storage technology is used to collect CO_2 from fossil-fuel power stations before it is released into the atmosphere. This reduces the amount of CO_2 building up in the atmosphere and reduces the strength of the greenhouse effect.

Q5 a) reflection

b)

TV remote sensor

mirror

r
i

normal

TV remote

angle of incidence, i = angle of reflection, r

Q6 a) The 'spare' electricity can be used to pump water up to a higher reservoir, which can then be released quickly during periods of peak demand to generate electricity.

b) E.g. increase supply by opening more power plants, increase supply by increasing the power output of power plants, consumers reducing their demands.

Q7 a) Diffraction

b) It will diffract the most when the gap is the same size as the wavelength. If the gap is much wider than the wavelength, it will only diffract a little.

c) Water molecules can absorb some wavelengths of microwave. If the water in question happens to be in your cells, e.g. brain cells, this may cause cell damage / your brain might start to cook.

Q8 a) 0.02 m

b) 10 Hz

c) speed = wavelength × frequency = 0.02 × 10 = **0.2 m/s**

Q9 a) The gas is burned to convert its stored chemical energy into heat energy. The heat is used to turn water into steam, which drives turbines. Generators then convert the kinetic energy of the turbine blades into electrical energy.

b) i) nuclear energy, biofuel

ii) Both solar and wind power are unreliable / dependent on the weather. / On days which weren't sunny or windy, there would be little or no electricity.

c) i) So that the current required to transmit power can be low, which reduces the energy wasted through heating in the cables.

ii) The high voltage is 'stepped down' using a series of transformers before it reaches people's homes or businesses.

Q10 a)

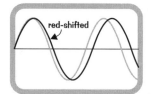

red-shifted

b) More distant galaxies have greater red-shifts than nearer ones, showing that more distant galaxies are moving away from us faster. This is evidence that the universe is expanding and started in a very dense (and hot) state.

Physics 2a — Motion, Energy and Electricity

Page 53 — Velocity and Distance-Time Graphs

Q1 −12 m/s

Q2 a) 180 s (or 3 mins)

b) Speed = gradient of graph = distance ÷ time
Speed = 450 ÷ 180 = 2.5 m/s

c) He runs there in half the time it took him to walk there — 90 s. So the graph looks like this:

Distance (m)

Time (s)

Q3 The graph shows that the motorist accelerates for about 1.5 seconds, then travels at a constant speed. So the gradient of the graph between 1.5 s and 3.0 s will give you the speed.
Gradient = vertical change ÷ horizontal change = (72 − 18) ÷ (3.0 − 1.5) = 54 ÷ 1.5 = **36 m/s** — i.e. she was exceeding the speed limit. So the motorist wasn't telling the truth.

Pages 54-55 — Acceleration and Velocity-Time Graphs

Q1 a) The car accelerates from rest, so the change in velocity is **20 m/s**.
Acceleration = change in velocity ÷ time taken = 20 ÷ 3.5 = **5.7 m/s²**.

b) Change in velocity = 20 − 3 = 17 m/s.
So acceleration = 17 ÷ 2.8 = **6.1 m/s²**.
The car has a greater acceleration than before. (This assumes that the modified car's acceleration from 0 to 3 m/s is not slower.)

Q2 a) Since the egg was dropped from rest, its change in speed is 80 m/s. So acceleration = 80 ÷ 8 = **10 m/s²**.

b) Now rearrange the formula to get time taken
Time taken = change in velocity ÷ acceleration = 40 ÷ 10 = **4 s**

Q3 Rearranging the formula for acceleration you get:
change in speed = acceleration × time = 2 × 4 = 8 m/s.
Change in speed = final speed − initial speed, so initial speed = final speed − change in speed = 24 − 8 = **16 m/s**.

Q4 Acceleration = gradient = 8 ÷ 5 = **1.6 m/s²**.

Physics 2a — Motion, Energy and Electricity

Q5 A — (constant) acceleration (from 0 - 3 m/s)
B — constant speed (of 3 m/s)
C — (constant) acceleration (from 3 - 9 m/s)
D — constant speed (of 9 m/s)
E — (constant) deceleration (from 9 - 7 m/s)

Q6 The distance the bus driver travelled before stopping is equal to the area under the graph. To find it, split the graph into a rectangle and a triangle.
Area of the rectangle = base × height = 0.75 × 12 = 9 m.
Area of the triangle = half × base × height = 0.5 × 2.5 × 12 = 15 m. Total distance = 9 m + 15 m = **24 m**.
He didn't hit the piglet.

Page 56 — Weight, Mass and Gravity

Q1 mass, kilograms, weight, newtons, gravitational
Q2 a) W = m × g
m = 58 kg, g = 10 N/kg
W = 58 × 10 = **580 N**
b) Change in weight = 580 − 460 = 120 N
Change in mass = change in weight ÷ g
= 120 ÷ 10 = **12 kg**
Q3a) Mass is the amount of matter, which stays constant. Weight is the force of gravity on this mass, and as the gravity is a different strength on Mars her weight changes.
b) Mass = weight ÷ gravitational field strength, which on Earth is 10 N/kg, so the rock has a mass of 5 kg.
1.9 kg ÷ 5 kg = 0.38
The scales read 38% of the true mass, so the gravitational field strength on Mars is 38% of that on Earth. 10 N/kg × 0.38 = **3.8 N/kg** (or m/s^2).

Page 57 — Resultant Forces

Q1 a) The teapot's weight is balanced by a reaction force from the table.
b) i) No. The teapot is accelerating so the forces can't be balanced.
ii) The reaction force from the floor.
Q2 a)

b) No — he is decelerating. South.
Q3 a) 1 500 000 − 1 500 000 = 0 N
b) 6 000 000 − 1 500 000 = 4 500 000 N
Q4 a) There is a resultant force — the ball is slowing down, which is deceleration.
b) There is a resultant force — motion in a circle means constantly changing direction, which requires acceleration.
c) There is no resultant force — the vase is stationary on the window ledge.

Pages 58-60 — Forces and Acceleration

Q1 balanced, stationary, constant, non-zero, accelerates, resultant force, interact, opposite
Q2 The third statement should be ticked — The driving force of the engine is equal to friction and air resistance combined.

Q3 a) Statement **C** should be circled — The thrust is equal to the air resistance and the lift is equal to the weight.
b) i) The thrust is **less than** the air resistance.
ii) The lift is **less than** the weight.
Q4 Force = mass × acceleration.
Disraeli 9000: 800 kg × 5 m/s^2 = 4000 N
Palmerston 6i: 1560 kg × 0.7 m/s^2 = 1092 N
Heath TT: 950 kg × 3 m/s^2 = 2850 N
Asquith 380: 790 kg × 2 m/s^2 = 1580 N
So the correct order is: **Palmerston 6i, Asquith 380, Heath TT, Disraeli 9000**.
Q5 a) The force of the engine is 110 kg × 2.80 m/s^2 = **308 N**.
b) Mass = force ÷ acceleration = 308 ÷ 1.71 = **180 kg** (to 3 s.f.).
Q6 Using F = ma, the resultant force on the mass must be 1 kg × 0.25 m/s^2 = 0.25 N.
Resultant force = force on the newton-meter − force of friction (they act in opposite directions).
0.25 N = 0.4 N − force of friction, so force of friction = 0.4 N − 0.25 N = **0.15 N**.
Q7 The third statement should be ticked — The car's pulling force accelerates the caravan. The caravan's reaction acts on the car, not the caravan.
Q8 The first statement should be ticked — Your feet push backwards on the ground, so the ground pushes you forwards.
Q9a) i) The van is travelling at a steady speed, so the resultant force must be 0. So the force exerted by the engine must be equal to the air resistance and friction combined.
2000 N + 500 N = **2500 N**.
ii)

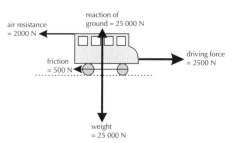

air resistance = 2000 N
reaction of ground = 25 000 N
driving force = 2500 N
friction = 500 N
weight = 25 000 N

b) The resultant force will now be 200 N (forces were previously balanced)
a = F/m = 200 ÷ 2500 = **0.08 m/s^2**.
c) The resultant force is now maximum driving force − (force of wind + friction + air resistance) = 2650 − 2700 = −50 N. This force acts in the opposite direction to the van's movement, so the van will continue to decelerate, but at a slower rate (0.02 m/s^2).

Pages 61-62 — Frictional Force and Terminal Velocity

Q1 greater, accelerates, increase, balances, constant, greater, decelerates, decrease, balances, constant.
Q2 All the boxes except 'carrying less cargo' should be ticked.
Q3 a) Paola is **wrong** because although gravity (the accelerating force per unit mass) is the same for both objects, air resistance will affect them differently because they have different shapes.
b) Guiseppe is **right** because drag will be greater for the feather compared to its weight, so drag will balance its weight sooner. The hammer will continue to accelerate for longer than the feather.
Q4 No, Mavis can't draw any conclusions.
The terminal velocity depends not only on drag (which is determined by the size, shape and smoothness of the object) but on the weight of the object, and the weights of the balls will be different.

Physics 2a — Motion, Energy and Electricity

Q5 Region A: weight is greater
Region B: both equal
Region C: air resistance is greater
Region D: both equal

Q6 a) No, Kate isn't really moving upwards. She only **seems** to move upwards when she opens her parachute because she slows down relative to the camera (which is held by Alison — who hasn't opened her parachute yet).

b) She decelerates until she reaches her terminal velocity and then falls at this speed until she lands.

Q7 a) Venus's atmosphere is much thicker than Earth's so a parachute the same size or smaller would provide enough drag to slow the probe to a safe speed.

b) Mars has lower gravity, so less drag is required to balance the probe's weight, but there is much less resistance from the thinner atmosphere, so the parachute would have to be larger than one used on Earth.

Page 63 — Stopping Distances

Q1 a) The distance the car travels under the braking force before it comes to a stop.

b) The distance the car travels during the driver's reaction time.

Q2

Thinking Distance	Braking Distance
tiredness	road surface
alcohol	tyres
speed	weather
drugs	brakes
	speed
	load

Q3 The total stopping distance will increase. Both thinking and braking distance will increase.

Q4 The friction between the brake discs and pads will be reduced if they are covered in water. This means the braking force will be reduced and the car will take longer to stop (i.e. the braking distance increases).

Q5 E.g. distractions like mobile phones won't affect Sam's thinking distance, as thinking distance is the distance travelled between the driver first spotting a hazard and taking action. However, it will mean that she will be less likely to notice a hazard until she is much closer to it. (So she is much more likely to crash if there is a hazard.)

Pages 64-65 — Work and Potential Energy

Q1 a) Work done and energy transferred are the same thing, so Jenny does **50 J** of work.

b) Distance = work done ÷ force = $50 \div 250 = \textbf{0.2 m}$

Q2 To push your bicycle you need to apply a force to overcome resistant forces like friction. The work done is equal to the force you apply (in the direction of motion) multiplied by the distance you push your bike.

Q3 a) True
b) False
c) True
d) True
e) False ($E_p = m \times g \times h = 3 \times 10 \times 2.5 = \textbf{75 J}$)

Q4 a) $E_p = m \times g \times h = 25 \text{ kg} \times 10 \text{ N/kg} \times 1.2 \text{ m} = \textbf{300 J}$.
b) Total $E_p = 28 \times 300 \text{ J} = \textbf{8400 J}$.
c) The energy transferred and the work done by Dave are the same thing, so **8400 J**.

Q5 a) Distance = work done ÷ force = $80\,000 \div 50 \text{ N} = \textbf{1600 m}$
b) i) Work = force × distance, so force = work ÷ distance = $90\,000 \div 120 = \textbf{750 N}$. weight / gravity

ii) Work = gravitational potential energy = mass × g × height, so mass = work ÷ (g × height)
mass = $90\,000 \div (10 \times 120) = \textbf{75 kg}$
(OR: Weight = mass × g so mass = weight ÷ g = $750 \div 10 = \textbf{75 kg}$)

Q6 a) Rearrange E_p = mass × g × height: height = $E_p \div (m \times g) = 4000 \div (50 \times 10) = 8 \text{ m}$
b) The energy converted from potential energy to kinetic energy is 1500 J, so the difference must be the wasted energy. $4000 \text{ J} - 1500 \text{ J} = \textbf{2500 J}$.
c) friction
d) Force = work ÷ distance = $2500 \div 50 = \textbf{50 N}$
e) Energy wasted = $4000 \text{ J} - 2000 \text{ J} = \textbf{2000 J}$.
Force = $2000 \div 50 = \textbf{40 N}$
f) The mat reduces the amount of friction. Less energy is wasted and so more potential energy is converted into kinetic energy.
g) Force = $2000 \div 5 = \textbf{400 N}$

Page 66 — Kinetic Energy

Q1 a) true
b) false
c) true

Q2 a) Just before the ball hits the ground, it has converted all of its potential energy into kinetic energy, so it has **242 J** of kinetic energy.
b) $v = \sqrt{\dfrac{2 \times E_k}{m}} = \sqrt{\dfrac{2 \times 242}{0.1}} = 69.6 \text{ m/s}$

Q3 a) i) $v = \sqrt{\dfrac{2 \times E_k}{m}} = \sqrt{\dfrac{2 \times 614\,400}{1200}} = 32 \text{ m/s}$

ii) $v = \sqrt{\dfrac{2 \times E_k}{m}} = \sqrt{\dfrac{2 \times 614\,400}{12\,288}} = 10 \text{ m/s}$

b) The **car** has more kinetic energy — doubling speed increases K.E. by a factor of 4 whereas trebling mass only increases K.E. by a factor of 3.

Q4 a) Distance = work done by brakes / force = $1440 \div 200 = \textbf{7.2 m}$.
b) The temperature of the brakes increases because the kinetic energy of the wheels is transferred to the heat energy of the brakes.

Page 67 — Forces and Elasticity

Q1 a) E.g. if something is elastic it means that when a force is applied it changes its shape and stores the work as elastic potential energy. When the force is removed the elastic object can return to its original shape.
b) The kinetic energy is transferred into the elastic potential energy of the springs around the trampoline as they stretch (as well as a bit of heat and sound energy).
c) i) $600 \div 30 = \textbf{20 N}$ per spring
ii) F = k × e
Rearranging gives: k = F ÷ e = $20 \div 0.1 = \textbf{200 N/m}$.

Q2 a) F = k × e
F = $45 \times 15 = \textbf{675 N}$
b) i) The limit of proportionality.
ii) The limit of proportionality has been reached so force is no longer proportional to extension, and the graph curves.

Physics 2a — Motion, Energy and Electricity

Pages 68-69 — Power

Q1   rate, energy, watts, joules, one hundred, light/ heat, heat/light

Q2 a)   Power = energy ÷ time, P = E ÷ t
       (Or equivalent, e.g. E = P × t.)

b)   Rearrange the formula to get energy = power × time.
       The car gets 50 000 × 5 × 60 = **15 000 000 J** of energy
       (= 15 000 kJ / 15 MJ).

c)   Power = energy transferred ÷ time taken
       = 144 000 ÷ (12 × 60) = **200 W**

Q3   Gravitational potential energy = mass × g × height.

   a) i)   46 × 10 × 5 = **2300 J**.

     ii)   48 × 10 × 5 = **2400 J**.

   b)   Power = work done ÷ time
       Catherine's power = 2300 ÷ 6.2 = **371 W**.
       Sally's power = 2400 ÷ 6.4 = **375 W**.
       Sally generated more power.

Q4 a)   Time in seconds = 10 × 60 = 600 s.
       Energy = power × time = 150 × 600 = **90 000 J** (= 90 kJ).

b)   90 kJ ÷ 30 kJ/ml = **3 ml**.

c)   Power = energy ÷ time = 120 000 ÷ (10 × 60) = **200 W**

Q5 a)   Josie is carrying her school bag so her total mass
       is 66 kg. The energy transferred by Josie is the
       kinetic energy she gains from her acceleration.
       K.E = ½ × m × v² = 0.5 × 66 × 8² = 2112 J
       Power = energy transferred ÷ time taken
       = 2112 ÷ 6 = **352 W**

b)   Josie puts down her school bag so her total mass is now
       only 60 kg. This time the energy is the gravitational
       potential energy she gains going up the stairs.
       E$_p$ = m × g × h = 60 × 10 × 5 = 3000 J
       P = E ÷ t = 3000 J ÷ 4 = **750 W**

Q6 a)   Start 4 – this wasn't a fair test because he slipped.

b)   Remembering to ignore start 4 —
       average time = **3.2 s**, average speed = **8.0 m/s**.

c)   E.g. calculate the power for each start, e.g. for sprint 1
       power = (1/2 × 70 × 8²) / 3.2 = 700 W.
       Then average these powers. 2804 ÷ 4 = **701 W**.

Page 70 — Momentum and Collisions

Q1 a)   If the velocity of a moving object doubles,
       its **momentum** will double.

b)   If you drop a suitcase out of a moving car, the car's
       momentum will **decrease**.

c)   When two objects collide the total
       momentum **stays the same**.

d)   When a force acts on an object its momentum **changes**.

Q2   Truck A's momentum = 30 m/s × 3000 kg
       = 90 000 kg m/s.
       Truck B's momentum = 10 m/s × 4500 kg
       = 45 000 kg m/s.
       Truck C's momentum = 20 m/s × 4000 kg
       = 80 000 kg m/s.
       Truck D's momentum = 15 m/s × 3500 kg
       = 52 500 kg m/s.
       So the order of increasing momentum is: **B, D, C, A**.

Q3 a)

b)   **Before** the collision:
       Trolley A's momentum = 10 kg × 4 m/s = 40 kg m/s.
       Trolley B's momentum = 30 kg × (–1 m/s) = –30 kg m/s.
       (Note the minus sign for trolley B's velocity because it's
       travelling in the opposite direction to trolley A.)
       So total momentum = 40 + (–30) = 10 kg m/s.
       After the collision:
       The joined trolleys have mass 40 kg and velocity v.
       Momentum$_{before}$ = momentum$_{after}$ = 10 kg m/s = 40 kg × v
       So, v = 10 kg m/s ÷ 40 kg = **+0.25 m/s**.
       The '+' sign shows that the joined trolleys
       travel in the same direction that trolley A
       was originally moving (i.e. east).

Pages 71-72 — Car Design and Safety

Q1   work, heat, regenerative, reverse, electric
       generator, chemical, efficient

Q2 a)   Kinetic energy.

b)   The brakes convert the kinetic energy into other
       forms of energy — mostly heat energy.

Q3   E.g. a roof box will make the car less aerodynamic
       and will increase the air resistance. The air resistance
       will therefore equal the driving force at lower
       speeds and the top speed will be reduced.

Q4 a)   E.g. by slowing the car and passengers down over a longer
       period of time, you spread out the change in momentum
       and reduce the force that the passengers experience.
       OR: you decrease the size of the deceleration. This
       reduces the forces on the car and passengers (F = ma),
       leading to less severe injuries for the passengers.

b)   E.g. any two from:
       Crumple zones – these crumple in a collision
       and convert some of the car's kinetic energy into
       heat and sound energy as it changes shape.
       Side impact bars – these direct the kinetic energy
       of a crash away from the passengers and towards
       other parts of the car, such as the crumple zones.
       Airbags – transfer part of the passenger's kinetic
       energy to the gas inside the airbag which escapes
       through pores in the material. (They also prevent the
       passenger from hitting hard surfaces within the car.)

Q5 a)   A seat belt absorbs kinetic energy as the
       material of the belt stretches.

b)   When a car crashes it changes velocity very suddenly. This
       means that there is a large momentum change which can
       mean a very large force on the passenger. By slowing down
       that change in momentum, the seat belt reduces the force
       on the internal organs, reducing the likelihood of injury.

Q6   Convert time in hours to time in seconds:
       1 hour = 60 mins = 60 × 60 s = 3600 s
       P = E ÷ t = 2 650 000 000 ÷ 3600 = **736 111 W** = (736 kW)

Physics 2a — Motion, Energy and Electricity

Page 73 — Static Electricity

Q1 Circled: positive and negative, negative and positive.
Underlined: negative and negative, positive and positive.

Q2 static, insulating, friction, electrons, positive / negative, negative / positive

Q3 a) A polythene rod becomes negatively charged when rubbed with a duster because it **gains** electrons.

b) When a negatively charged object and a positively charged object are brought together, **both** the **objects exert** a force **on each other**.

c) The closer two charged objects are together, the **more** strongly they attract or repel.

d) Electrical charges **can** move very easily through metals.

Q4 Electrons are transferred between the jumper and his hair, leaving his hair electrically charged. Because all the strands of hair have the same charge they repel one another — and stand on end.

Page 74 — Current and Potential Difference

Q1 charge, voltage, work, reduces, decrease

Q2 A — Current — amps
V — Potential Difference — volts
Ω — Resistance — ohms

Q3 a) Q = I × t
t = 20 × 60 = 1200 seconds
5 × 1200 = **6000 C**

b) W = V × Q
3 × 6000 = **18 000 J** (or **18 kJ**)

Q4

	Lamp A	Lamp B
Current through lamp (A)	2	4
Voltage drop across lamp (V)	3	2
Charge passing in 10 s (C)	20	40
Work done in 10 s (J)	60	80

Q5 a) Q = I × t
4 × (7 × 60) = **1680 C**

b) W = V × Q
9 × 1680 = **15 120 J** (or **15.12 kJ**)

Page 75 — Circuits — The Basics

Q1 Cell — Provides the 'push' on the charge.
Variable Resistor — Used to alter the current.
Component — The item you're testing.
Voltmeter — Measures the voltage.
Ammeter — Measures the current.

Q2 circuit, through, across

Q3 a) 1. Battery
2. Thermistor
3. Component / Fixed resistor
4. LDR
5. Switch (closed)
6. Filament Lamp

b) The ammeter must be drawn in series between the battery and the first junction.

c) The voltmeter must be drawn in parallel around the lamp.

Pages 76-77 — Resistance and V = I × R

Q1 A — Filament lamp
B — Diode
C — Resistor

Q2 a) False
b) True
c) False
d) True
e) True

Q3 a) D
b) Gradient = 4 ÷ 2 = **2**.
c) Resistance = 1 ÷ gradient = 1 ÷ 2 = **0.5 Ω**.

Q4 The heat energy causes the ions in the bulb's filament to vibrate more. This makes it more difficult for charge-carrying electrons to get through the filament, so the current can't flow as easily — the resistance increases.

Q5

Voltage (V)	Current (A)	Resistance (Ω)
6	2	**3**
8	**4**	2
9	3	3
4	8	**0.5**
2	**0.5**	4
1	0.5	2

Q6 a)

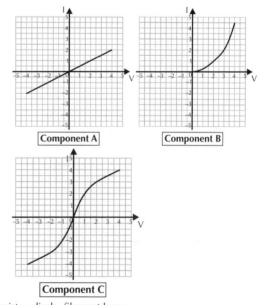

b) Resistor, diode, filament lamp

Physics 2a — Motion, Energy and Electricity

Page 78 — Circuit Devices

Q1 vary, thermistor, thermostats, light-dependent, lights

Q2 a) An LED emits light when a current flows through it in the forward direction.

b) LEDs use a much smaller current than other types of lighting (so they are cheaper to use).

Q3 a) E.g.

b) The resistance decreases.

c) The brightness of the lamp decreases.

Pages 79-80 — Series Circuits

Q1 Same everywhere in the circuit — Current.
Shared by all the components — Total potential difference.
The sum of the resistances — Total resistance.
Can be different for each component — Potential difference.

Q2 a) 1. The voltmeter is in series.
2. The ammeter is in parallel with the lamp.
3. The current is shown going the wrong way.
(Answers can be in any order.)

b)

Q3 a) $2\,V + 2\,V + 2\,V = \textbf{6 V}$

b) $V = I \times R$, so total R = total $V \div$ total $I = 6 \div 0.5 = \textbf{12 } \Omega$

c) R_3 = total resistance $- R_1 - R_2 = 12 - 2 - 4 = \textbf{6 } \Omega$

d) $V = I \times R = 0.5 \times 4 = \textbf{2 V}$

Q4 a) The lamps get dimmer as more are added because the voltage is shared out between the lamps.

b) The current gets smaller as more lamps are added. Each lamp adds more resistance which means less current.

Q5 a) E.g.

b) It decreases

c) Total resistance = resistance from resistor + resistance from motor = $1\Omega + 2\Omega = 3\Omega$.
$V = I \times R$, so $I = V \div R = 6 \div 3 = \textbf{2A}$.

Pages 81-82 — Parallel Circuits

Q1 a) True

b) True

c) False

d) True

Q2

Q3 1. 6 V
2. $4\,A - 3\,A = \textbf{1 A}$
3. 6 V

Q4 a) Nothing, because each lamp gets its voltage from the battery separately.

b) It increases because the currents to each lamp add up.

c) Nothing happens to the brightness of the other lamps.
(The answers above assume that the internal resistance of the cell is ignored — in practice the current would decrease a little as lamps were added.)

Q5 a) E.g. no, you can have a different current in each branch, but the voltage is always the same.

b) E.g. so that the lights can be switched on and off independently. / So that if one light fails, the others will still light up.

Pages 83-84 — Series and Parallel Circuits — Examples

Q1 Series Circuits
end to end
the same everywhere
shared between components
e.g. Christmas tree lights
Parallel Circuits
side by side
can be different in each branch
the same for each component
e.g. car electrics, household electrics (or any other sensible answer)

Q2 a) If they were wired in parallel, the bulbs would be 230 V because each one would get the full voltage.

b) They don't all go off if one fails / you can tell which one has failed.

c) The bulbs will be designed to work at different voltages. In parallel 230 V bulbs are needed (although in practice transformers are often used to lower the voltage). In series the bulbs used are suitable for smaller voltages e.g. 12 V because the voltage is shared.

Q3 $V_0 = \textbf{12 V}$, $A_1 = \textbf{1 A}$, $V_1 = I \times R = 1 \times 4 = \textbf{4 V}$,
$V_3 = 12\,V - 4\,V - 2\,V = \textbf{6 V}$

Q4 a) i) $I = V \div R = 12 \div 2 = \textbf{6 A}$

ii) $I = V \div R = 12 \div 4 = \textbf{3 A}$

b) i) **12 V**

ii) **12 V**

c) $A_0 = A_2 + A_3 = 3\,A + 2\,A = \textbf{5 A}$

Q5 1. If the engine isn't running the battery might not be able to provide enough current for the fan and lights together at full voltage. So the lights might be slightly dimmer.
2. If the bulbs are in series, taking one out will break the circuit and all the bulbs will go out.
3. The wall lamps are in parallel but they share the same switch.

Pages 85-87— Mixed Questions — Physics 2a

Q1 a) Work done = force $\times$ distance = 300×1500 = **450 000 J** (or 450 kJ).

b) Acceleration = change in speed $\div$ time taken = $20 \div 6.2 = \textbf{3.23 m/s}^2$ (to 3 s.f.).

c) This will reduce the top speed of the car — the air resistance against the car will be increased, and so will equal the maximum driving force at a lower speed.

d) A seat belt will increase the time over which there is a momentum change, so he will experience a smaller force.

Physics 2b — Electricity and the Atom

Q2 a) $E_p = m \times g \times h = 12\,000 \times 34 = \textbf{408 000 J}$ (= 408 kJ).

b) Two thirds of the potential energy is converted into kinetic energy, so gain in $E_k = 408\,000 \times 2/3$
= 272 000 J. Two thirds of the way down, speed =
$$v = \sqrt{\frac{2 \times E_k}{m}} = \sqrt{\frac{2 \times 272\,000}{1200}} = \textbf{21.3 m/s} \text{ (3 s.f.)}$$

c) Time = speed ÷ acceleration = 20 ÷ 6.4 = **3.125 s**.

Q3 a) 10 + 5 + 5 = **20 Ω**.

b) i) $I = V \div R = 4 \div 10 = \textbf{0.4 A}$ (current through 10 Ω resistor is the same as current in all parts of the circuit).

ii) $V = I \times R = 0.4 \times 20 = \textbf{8 V}$.

Q4 a) 120 s − 60 s = **60 s** (1 minute).

b) Train 1 is faster.
Speed = gradient = 50 ÷ 40 = **1.25 m/s**.

c) E.g. train 1 is decelerating / has a negative acceleration / is slowing down.

Q5 a) No — the car is not changing speed or direction / not accelerating and so there cannot be a resultant force.

b) 90 km/h = 90 000 ÷ 3600 = 25 m/s.
momentum = m × v = 2100 × 25 = **52 500 kg m/s**

c) i) E.g. how tired she is / how fast she is driving / whether she had consumed alcohol / whether she had consumed drugs etc.

ii) F = change in momentum ÷ time = 52 500 ÷ 3.0 = **17 500 N**

Q6 a) i) 4 × 0.5 = **2.0 A**.

ii) 0 A

iii) (4 × 0.5) + (2 × 6.0) = **14.0 A**.

b) Thermistor — they are a temperature dependent resistor. The resistance of a thermistor decreases as temperature increases and increases as temperature decreases.

Q7 a) As soon as it's dropped the dummy accelerates under the influence of gravity. So as it falls its velocity increases steadily. When it hits the ground its velocity changes almost instantly to zero and stays at zero.

b) i) Work done = potential energy gained
= m × g × h = 95 × 10 × 60 = **57 000 J** (or 57 kJ).

ii) Time = work ÷ power = 57 000 ÷ 760 = **75 s**.

c) Weight of dummy = m × g = 95 × 10 = 950 N
k = F ÷ e = 950 ÷ 5 = **190 N/m**

Q8 a) her weight / gravity

b) 700 N

c) There is now a resultant force on her, acting upwards. This accelerates her upwards, reducing her downward velocity.

d) 700 N

Physics 2b — Electricity and the Atom

Page 88 — Mains Electricity

Q1 volts, alternating, a.c., direction, changing, frequency, hertz, batteries, direct, d.c., same

Q2 a) C

b) B

c) A

Q3 a) 2 volts

b) 4 × 10 ms = **40 ms** or **0.04 s**

c) Frequency = 1 ÷ 0.04 = **25 Hz**

Page 89 — Electricity in the Home

Q1 There should be rings round: cable over cooker, overloaded socket, cable over sink, sockets too near the sink, long cable on the floor, hamster chewing the cable, child sitting on worktop sticking a fork in the socket, lamp that could easily be knocked over.

Q2 a) Because these materials are electrical insulators.

b) These materials are electrical conductors, and are used for those parts that the electricity goes through.

c) Rubber or plastic because they are electrical insulators and are flexible.

Q3 a) insulation

b) live

c) neutral

d) green and yellow, earth

e) firmly, bare

f) outer

Q4 1. The earth wire isn't connected.
2. Bare wires are showing.
3. The neutral and live wires are the wrong way round.

Page 90 — Fuses and Earthing

Q1 The live and neutral wires should normally carry the same current.
A circuit breaker does the same job as a fuse.
A Residual Current Circuit Breaker can be used instead of a fuse and earth wire.
Any metal casing should be connected to the earth wire.
A fuse melts when the current in a fuse wire exceeds the rating of the fuse.

Q2 1. A fault allows the live wire to touch the metal case.
2. A big current flows out through the earth wire.
3. A big surge in current blows the fuse.
4. The device is isolated from the live wire.

Q3 a) When an RCCB detects a difference in the current between the live and neutral wires it turns off the power by opening a switch.

b) E.g. any two from: They work much faster than fuses. / They work even for small current changes that might not be large enough to melt a fuse. / They can easily be reset whereas fuses need to be replaced once used.

Q4 a) **2 A.** (It's nearest to the actual current but still higher so that it won't blow with normal use.)

b) Because it has an insulated case with no metal parts showing.

c) two-core cable

d) They both increase with current size — the bigger the current, the higher the fuse rating needs to be and the thicker the cable needs to be to carry it.

Page 91 — Energy and Power in Circuits

Q1 how long, power, energy, time, heat, more

Q2 a) E.g. most of the energy is wasted as heat.

b) E.g. it's more energy efficient (so cheaper to run).

c) E.g. he might think it is more cost effective to buy a cheaper bulb even though the running costs will be more (he may not plan on using the light bulb very much).

Q3 a) 1000 J, light, heat

b) 60 000 J, kinetic, heat, sound

c) 20 000 J, heat

d) 1 200 000 J, heat

Physics 2b — Electricity and the Atom

Page 92 — Power and Energy Change

Q1 a)

	Lamp A	Lamp B	Lamp C
Voltage (V)	12	3	230
Current (A)	2.5	4	0.1
Power (W)	30	12	23
Energy used in one minute (J)	1800	720	1380

b) A = 3 A, B = 5 A, C = 1 A.

Q2 a) Current = power ÷ voltage = 1500 ÷ 230 = 6.5 A

b) 7 A

Q3

	Drill A	Drill B
Current through drill (A)	2	3
Voltage drop across drill (V)	230	230
Charge passing in 5 s (C)	10	15
Energy transformed in 5 s (J)	2300	3450

Q4 a) $Q = I \times t$
$0.6 \times (12 \times 60) =$ **432 C**

b) $W = V \times Q$
$2 \times 432 =$ **864 J**

Page 93 — Atomic Structure

Q1 a) no
b) ion
c) protons, electrons (in either order)
d) positively

Q2

Particle	Mass	Charge
Proton	1	+1
Neutron	1	0
Electron	very small	−1

Q3 a) i) They fired a beam of alpha particles at thin gold foil.
ii) They expected the positively charged alpha particles to be slightly deflected by the electrons in the plum pudding model.
b) Most of the alpha particles went straight through the foil, but the odd one came straight back at them. This showed that atoms are not like a plum pudding, they have a very small central nucleus with electrons orbiting round it. Most of the atom is empty space — the nucleus is tiny compared to the size of the atom. It also showed that the nucleus must have a large positive charge to have repelled the alpha particles by large angles.

Pages 94-95 — Atoms and Ionising Radiation

Q1 a) False
b) True
c) False
d) False
e) True

Q2 a) i) Background radiation.
ii) E.g. any two from: Nuclear weapon tests. / Nuclear accidents. / Dumped nuclear waste.
b) i) Background radiation is higher in Cornwall due to the type of rock underground.
ii) E.g. any one from: food / cosmic rays / building materials.
iii) Yes. $(1000 \times 0.00001) + 0.008 = 0.018$.

Q3 Alpha particle — 2 neutrons and 2 protons — the same as a helium nucleus.
Beta particle — An electron from the nucleus.
Gamma radiation — A type of electromagnetic radiation.

Q4

Radiation Type	Ionising power weak/moderate/ strong	Charge positive/ none/ negative	Relative mass no mass/ small/large	Penetrating power low/moderate/ high	Range in air short/long/ very long
alpha	strong	positive	large	low	short
beta	moderate	negative	small	moderate	long
gamma	weak	none	no mass	high	very long

Q5 a) $^{234}_{90}\text{Th} \rightarrow ^{234}_{91}\text{Pa} + ^{0}_{-1}\text{e}$

b) $^{222}_{86}\text{Rn} \rightarrow ^{218}_{84}\text{Po} + ^{4}_{2}\alpha$

Q6 1. The particles move in opposite directions — this is because they have opposite charges.
2. The alpha particle is deflected less than the beta particle — this is because alpha particles have a much greater mass than beta particles.

Page 96 — Half-Life

Q1 In 60 years' time, the count rate will be half what it is now.

Q2 a) In 29 years time, the count rate will have halved — half of the radioactive nuclei will have decayed.
b) **125** (87 years is 3 half-lives.)

Q3 After 1 half-life: 720 cpm
After 2 half-lives: 360 cpm
After 3 half-lives: 180 cpm
After 4 half-lives: 90 cpm
After 5 half-lives: 45 cpm
Therefore 5 hours is 5 half-lives.
So 1 half-life = **1 hour**.

Q4 a)

b) There will always be some background radiation (in this case it looks like approx. 100 cpm) AND the radioactivity of the sample will never fall to zero.
c) The background radiation must be subtracted from her readings. The count therefore starts at 640. Half of that is 320 (or 420 including background radiation). This occurs on the 20th minute.

Page 97 — Uses of Radiation

Q1 1. The radioactive source emits alpha particles.
2. The air between the electrodes is ionised by the alpha particles.
3. A current flows between the electrodes — the alarm stays off.
4. A fire starts and smoke particles absorb the alpha radiation.
5. The circuit is broken so no current flows.
6. The alarm sounds.

Physics 2b — Electricity and the Atom

Q2 a) A gamma-emitter with a long half-life is used. Gamma radiation is needed because it is not stopped by air or metal parts of the instruments and can kill the cells of living organisms (e.g. bacteria) on the instruments. A long half-life is needed because the sterilising machine will be in use over many years and replacing the source frequently would be inconvenient.

b) Lead is used to prevent the operator and anyone near the machine from getting too high a dose of radiation.

Q3 a) Technetium-99. It has the shortest half-life.

b) Cobalt-60. It emits gamma radiation, which can penetrate the body and can kill cancer cells. It has a fairly long half-life so the hospital would not need to replace the source too often.

Page 98 — Radioactivity Safety

Q1 a) E.g. he isn't wearing protective gloves. He isn't using tongs to handle the sample. He is pointing the sample directly into the face of the other scientist.

b) E.g. by minimising the time the samples are out of their boxes.

c) In a thick-walled, lead-lined container.

Q2 a) beta and gamma

b) i) alpha radiation

ii) It's highly ionising and can damage or kill cells in our bodies. A high dose can kill lots of cells at once, causing radiation sickness. It can also cause cancer when cells are damaged, mutate and divide uncontrollably.

Page 99 — Nuclear Fission and Fusion

Q1 uranium-235, split, heat, water, steam, turbine, generator, electricity

Q2 E.g. the slow-moving neutron is absorbed by a plutonium nucleus. This plutonium nucleus splits up, forming new lighter elements and spitting out two or three neutrons. One or more of these 'extra' neutrons may then be absorbed by another plutonium nucleus, causing it to split and spit out more neutrons, which may cause other nuclei to split etc.

Q3 E.g. any four from: Fission splits nuclei up, fusion combines nuclei. / Fission reactors use uranium or plutonium, fusion reactors use hydrogen. / Fission produces radioactive waste, fusion produces very little radioactive waste. / Fission reactors already exist, fusion reactors are still being developed. / Fusion requires extremely high temperatures, fission does not.

Q4 **Good points**
E.g. fuel is cheap and plentiful, they produce very little radioactive waste.
Bad points
E.g. no materials can stand the high temperatures needed, it requires a lot of energy to achieve such high temperatures.

Pages 100-101 — The Life Cycle of Stars

Q1 hot, fusion, stable, outwards, inwards, billions

Q2 a) Gravitational attraction pulls the material together.

b) Gas and dust in orbit around a newly formed star may clump together to form masses. The smaller masses are attracted to larger masses, and they eventually merge together to become planets.

Q3 a) A star becomes a red giant when the hydrogen fuel in its core begins to run out. (Hydrogen outside the core is burnt, heating the outer layers and causing the star to expand.)

b) It becomes red because its surface cools.

c) They cool and contract into a white dwarf and then when the light fades completely they become a black dwarf.

Q4 The explosion is called a supernova. The outer layers of dust and gas are thrown out into the universe. This leaves a very dense core known as a neutron star. If the star is big enough this can become a black hole.

Q5 A Clouds of Dust and Gas   B Protostar
C Main Sequence Star   D Red Giant
E White Dwarf   F Black Dwarf
G Red Super Giant   H Supernova
I Neutron Star   J Black Hole

Q6 a) New elements have been formed by fusion in stars.

b) They consume massive amounts of hydrogen.

c) They are formed when a big star explodes in a supernova and are ejected into the universe.

Pages 102-104 — Mixed Questions — Physics 2b

Q1 a) The nucleus of cobalt-60 contains one more neutron than that of cobalt-59.

b) medical tracers — technetium-99m
smoke detectors — americium-241
detecting leaks in pipes — technetium-99m or cobalt-60

c) i) gamma

ii) Because the radiation damages healthy normal cells as well as the cancerous ones.

d) Work out how many half-lives would be needed.
$120 \div 2^5 = 3.75$, so just under 5 half-lives would be needed to bring the count rate down to 4 cpm.
The half-life of americium-241 is 432 years.
$432 \times 5 = 2160$. So roughly **2000 years** would be needed.

e) Any two of: always handle the source with tongs. / Never allow the source to touch his skin. / Hold the source as far away from his body as possible. / Keep the source pointing away from his body. / Avoid looking directly at the source. / Store the source in a lead-lined box and put it away as soon as his experiment is finished.

Q2 a) nuclear fission

b) A neutron hits a uranium nucleus and is absorbed, giving the nucleus too many neutrons to be stable. It then decays into two smaller nuclei and some fast-moving neutrons, which go on to cause other uranium nuclei to undergo fission.

c) The heat from the reactor is used to make steam, which turns a turbine attached to a generator, which produces the electricity.

d) E.g. doesn't produce radioactive waste, there's plenty of hydrogen around to use as fuel.

e) At the moment it takes more power to create the right conditions in a reactor needed for fusion (e.g. high temperature) than the reactor can produce.

f) i) Stars consume huge amounts of hydrogen in nuclear fusion (which creates new elements).

ii) Heat created by nuclear fusion provides an outward pressure to balance the force of gravity pulling everything inwards.

Q3 a) A large current flows through the live wire, passes through the metal case and out down the earth wire. The large current causes the fuse to melt, which cuts off the live supply.

b) i) live, neutral

ii) It doesn't need an earth wire because the case is made of plastic and there are no metal parts exposed or which could touch the case.

Q4 a) A current that always keeps flowing in the same direction.

b) $I = P \div V = 600 \div 230 = 2.6$ (to 2 s.f)
So the fuse needed is a 3 A fuse.

c) The broken plastic casing may expose live parts which could give Kate an electric shock.

d) Time period = 10 ms $\times$ 3.5 = 0.01 $\times$ 3.5 = 0.035 s
Frequency = 1 $\div$ 0.035 = **29 Hz**.

Physics 3a — Medical Applications of Physics

Physics 3a — Medical Applications of Physics

Pages 105-106 — X-rays in Medicine

Q1 a) short, ionisation
b) transmitted, absorbed
c) charge-coupled device
d) atom

Q2 kill, cells, cancer, focused, normal, ill, rotating, centre

Q3 a) E.g. X-rays interact with photographic film in the same way as visible light. The X-ray image is formed by the varying intensities of X-ray beam that are transmitted (i.e. through soft tissue) through to the film. Where the X-rays are transmitted, more X-rays reach the photographic plate causing it to turn dark. This leaves a white image of the denser areas.
b) E.g. A charge-coupled device can be used to form a high resolution image. A CCD is a grid of millions of pixels, each of which is sensitive to X-rays. Each pixel generates an electric signal when it interacts with an X-ray.
c) E.g. bone fractures.

Q4 a) True
b) False
c) False
d) True

Q5 1. The patient is put inside the CT scanner.
2. An X-ray tube emits an X-ray beam whilst rotating around the patient.
3. Detectors on the opposite side of the scanner measure the intensity of the transmitted X-rays.
4. A computer uses the detected X-rays to generate an image of a two-dimensional slice through the body.
5. Multiple slice images are put together to give a three-dimensional picture.

Q6 a) E.g. any two from: wear a lead apron / stand behind a lead screen / leave the room.
b) E.g. any two from: minimise exposure time / avoid repeat X-rays / use lead to shield other areas of the body not being imaged.

Page 107 — Ultrasound

Q1 a) Ultrasound is sound with a frequency above 20 000 Hz — higher than the upper limit of hearing for humans.
b) Electrical devices can be set to produce electrical oscillations at the required frequency. These can be converted into mechanical vibrations (i.e. sound waves).

Q2 E.g.

Q3 a) Looking at the oscilloscope trace, there is a 5 μs gap between the start of the trace and the first ultrasound pulse.
$s = v \times t$
$v = 1450$ m/s, $t = 0.000005$ s
$s = 1450 \times 0.000005 = 0.00725$
You need to divide by 2 to find the distance between the ultrasound device and the fat boundary:
$0.00725 \div 2 = \mathbf{0.003625\ m}$ (= 0.36 cm).

b) The time between traces = 5×5 μs = 0.000025 s
Distance = speed × time = $1450 \times 0.000025 = 0.03625$ m
But this is the distance to travel through the layer of fat and back again so divide by 2 to find the thickness of the layer of fat: $0.03625 \div 2 = 0.018125$ m = **1.8 cm** (to 1 d.p.)

Page 108 — Ultrasound Uses

Q1 a) It breaks the kidney stones into small particles.
b) They pass out of the body in urine.
c) E.g. it's relatively painless, no surgery is required.

Q2 a)

	Advantage	Disadvantage
Ultrasound imaging	E.g. non-ionising, can image soft tissue	E.g. produces low resolution, fuzzy images
X-ray photographs	E.g. low radiation dose, can image hard tissue, e.g. bone, better resolution than ultrasound images	E.g. the radiation is ionising, images are limited to 2D
CT scans	E.g. produces high resolution images of both hard and soft tissue, can be used to make 3D images	E.g. high radiation dose, expensive

b) E.g. CT scanning, because a high resolution image of both the brain and the skull can be produced.

Q3 a) Ultrasound causes no known damage to cells, whereas X-rays are ionising radiation which can cause cancer.
b) X-rays — they penetrate most of the soft tissues but are absorbed (mostly) by bone. Ultrasound would not give a good picture of the bone as it would be reflected at the boundaries between different layers of soft tissue.

Page 109 — Refractive Index

Q1 a) refraction
b) E.g.

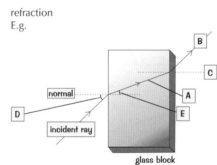

glass block

Q2 a) The ratio of the speed of light in a vacuum to the speed of light in that medium.
b) n = sin i / sin r
n – refractive index, i = angle of incidence, r – angle of refraction.

Q3 n = sin 30 ÷ sin 22 = **1.3**.
Q4 n = sin i / sin r, so 1.514 = sin 45 ÷ sin r.
Therefore sin r = sin 45 ÷ 1.514 = 0.467.
Hence r = $\sin^{-1}$ (0.467) = **27.8°**.

Pages 110-111 — Lenses and Images

Q1 a) W = incident
X = converging
Y = parallel
Z = focal point
b) The following statements should be ticked:
Any ray passing along the axis
Any ray passing through the centre of the lens

Q2 a) False
b) True
c) True
d) False

Physics 3a — Medical Applications of Physics

Q3 a) D — Either a converging or a diverging lens

b)

OR

Q4 a) In a real image, the rays from the object actually pass through the image (so it can be projected onto a screen). In a virtual image, the rays only appear to have come from the location of the image.

b) 1. say its size
2. say whether it is upright or inverted
3. say whether it is real or virtual.

Q5 a) The focal point on the other side of the lens.

b) Through the centre of the lens.

c) The top of the image will be where those two rays meet.

Q6

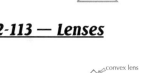

Pages 112-113 — Lenses

Q1

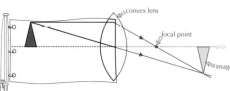

Q2 virtual, upright, smaller.

Q3 a)

Distance from lens to object	Distance from lens to image	Type of image	Size of image
Greater than 2F	Between 2F and F	Real, inverted	Smaller than object
Equal to 2F	**Equal to 2F**	Real, inverted	**Equal to object**
Between 2F and F	Greater than 2F	**Real, inverted**	**Larger than object**
Less than F	Greater than 2F	**Virtual, upright**	Larger than object

b) i) The image will be 1 cm high.
ii) The image will be 5 cm away from the lens on the opposite side from the object.

Q4 a) i) upright
ii) on the same side
iii) virtual

b) C – 10.2 cm

Q5

Q6

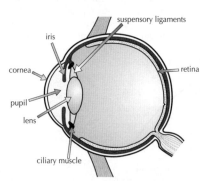

Pages 114-115 — Magnification and Power

Q1 a) A convex / converging lens

b) It is only at a distance nearer than the focal point that you will get an upright, magnified, virtual image.

c) B, D and E should be circled.

Q2 a) Magnification = image height ÷ object height

b) M = 0.8 ÷ 0.5 = 1.6

c) 3 × 1.6 = 4.8 mm

Q3 a) fatter lenses

b) power = 1 ÷ focal length

Q4 a) power = 1 ÷ focal length = 1 ÷ 0.15 = **6.67 D** (to 2 d.p.)

b) focal length = 1 ÷ power = 1 ÷ 5.2 = **0.19 m** (to 2 d.p.)

c) The **power** of a converging lens is **positive**, whereas the **power** of a diverging lens is **negative**.

Q5 a) 1. The curvature of the lens surfaces.
2. The refractive index of the lens material.

b) A material with a higher refractive index was used. For a given focal length, the greater the refractive index the flatter the lens. This means the lens can be manufactured to be thinner.

Pages 116-117 — The Eye

Q1

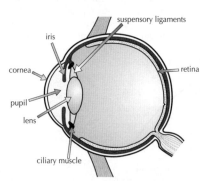

Q2a) Both are real, inverted images projected onto a "screen" (the film in the case of the camera, the retina in the case of the eye).

b) Because for an object nearer to a converging lens than the focal length, the image formed is virtual. A virtual image can't be projected onto the film.

c) on the film, smaller, retina

Physics 3a — Medical Applications of Physics

Q3

Part of the eye	Function
Lens	Focuses light on the retina
Retina	Light sensitive layer
Ciliary muscles	Cause the lens to change shape
Pupil	Hole through which light enters the eye

Q4 relax, thin, cornea, retina, retina

Q5 a) The near point is **the closest distance that the eye can focus on.**
For normally-sighted adults, the near point is about **25** cm.

b) The far point is **the furthest distance that the eye can focus on comfortably.**
For normally-sighted adults, the far point is at **infinity**.

Page 118 — Correcting Vision

Q1 a) short, far, far away, in front of

b) 1. Cornea and lens system is too powerful.
2. Eyeball is too long.

c) i) A

ii) A diverging lens of negative power compensates for an overly powerful lens and cornea system. The light from the object is diverged before it enters the eye so that the image is brought into focus at the retina. It makes objects an infinite distance away appear as though they are at the eye's natural far point.

Q2 a) A narrow intense beam of light.

b) i) To burn and seal shut tissue, e.g. blood vessels.

ii) E.g. a surgeon uses a laser to vaporise some of the cornea to change its shape. This can increase or decrease the power of the cornea, and so correct long or short sight.

Page 119 — Total Internal Reflection

Q1 a) Visible light.

b) Glass or perspex/plastic.

c) One bundle brings the light to the area/object in the body that needs to be looked at. The second bundle brings the light from the area/object back to form an image so the area can be viewed.

d) In the left-hand diagram, the angle of incidence is 46° (greater than the critical angle of 42°), so the ray is totally internally reflected. In the second diagram, the angle of incidence is 30°, so the ray is partially reflected, but most of the light passes out of the glass.

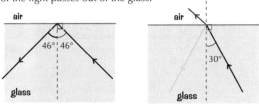

Q2 a) n = 1 ÷ sin c, c = 42°
n = 1 ÷ sin 42 = **1.49**

b) c = sin⁻¹ (1 ÷ n), n = 2.4
c = sin⁻¹ (1 ÷ 2.4) = **24.6°**

c) The diamond ring will be the most sparkly because it has the smaller critical angle, and so will totally internally reflect light from more angles than glass.

Pages 120-122 — Mixed Questions — Physics 3a

Q1 a) i) Medium 1 is glass
Medium 2 is air

ii) The light ray bends away from the normal as it enters medium 2, which shows its speed has increased. Light will speed up as it enters a less dense medium, which means medium 2 must be air.

b) i) B

ii) Total internal reflection occurs when light is travelling from a dense medium to a less dense medium. B is true because the light is travelling from glass to air — air is less dense than glass.

c) i) n = 1 ÷ sin c, c = 49°, n = 1 ÷ sin 49 = **1.33**

ii) n = sin i ÷ sin r, rearranging gives:
sin r = sin i ÷ n, r = sin⁻¹ (sin i ÷ n)
n = 1.33, i = 20°
r = sin⁻¹ (sin 20 ÷ 1.33) = **14.9°** (to 1 d.p.)

Q2 a)

b) short, behind, convex

c) i) Power = 1 ÷ focal length = 1 ÷ 0.4 = **2.5 D**

ii) The left lens is more powerful so will have a more strongly curved surface (the more curved the lens the greater its power).

d) i) 3 cm

ii) 4 ÷ 1.8 = 2.2

iii) Virtual — the light rays don't actually come from where they appear to, and the image can't be projected on a screen.

Q3 a) v = 1500 m/s
d = v × t = 1500 × 0.0000260 = 0.039 m
0.039 ÷ 2 = 0.0195 m ≈ **2 cm**.

b) E.g. X-rays are ionising and are therefore dangerous to the developing fetus. Ultrasound is non-ionising and, as far as anyone can tell, safe. (Ultrasound can image soft tissue whereas X-rays are more suited to imaging dense or hard tissue such as bone.)

c) E.g. X-rays are used to treat cancer because they are ionising. Large doses of ionising radiation can be used to kill cancerous cells. Ultrasound is non-ionising and won't damage cancerous cells.

d) E.g. CT scans use large doses of ionising X-rays which can be damaging to the health of the patient.

e) E.g. an **X-ray tube** fires intense beams of X-rays through the patient. These X-rays are picked up by **detectors** on the opposite side. The X-ray tube and detectors are **rotated** during the scan and a **computer** interprets the different intensities of X-ray signals to form an image of a two-dimensional **slice** of the patient. Multiple two-dimensional CT scans are compiled by the computer to form a three-dimensional image.

Physics 3b — Forces and Electromagnetism

Physics 3b — Forces and Electromagnetism

Pages 123-124 — Turning Forces and the Centre of Mass

Q1 a)   force, moment, perpendicular, pivot.
  b)   Nm (newton-metres)
Q2 a) $M = F \times d = 45 \times 0.1 = 4.5$ Nm
  b) i)   B
    ii)   C
Q3 a)

The centre of mass must fall on this line

  b)   centre of mass, vertically below, perpendicular, moment.
Q4 a)

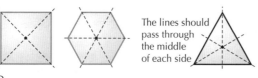

The lines should pass through the middle of each side

  b)   D
Q5   The weight of the pole acts at its centre of mass.
    The centre of mass of the pole is 0.4 m from each end.
    So the weight of 130 N acts 0.4 m from the pivot.
    $M = F \times d = 130 \times 0.4 = 52$ Nm
Q6 a)   Hang the plumb line from the same point as the piece of card. Draw a pencil line on the card along the plumb line. Hang the card in a different position and do the same thing again.
    Where the two lines cross is the centre of mass.
  b)   Preferred answer: Repeat the same steps for several pivot points to get multiple lines that will all cross at the centre of mass.
    Other acceptable answers: make sure the card is not swaying when the lines are marked / is not moved by marking the lines / is not bent out of shape; make sure the line isn't too thick and is accurately placed.

Page 125 — Balanced Moments and Levers

Q1 a) $M = F \times d = 2 \times 0.2 = 0.4$ Nm anticlockwise.
  b) $M = F \times d = 5 \times 0.16 = 0.8$ Nm anticlockwise.
  c)   Total anticlockwise moments = total clockwise moments.
    0.4 Nm + 0.8 Nm = 8 N × distance
    1.2 Nm = 8 N × distance
    1.2 ÷ 8 = distance
    distance = 0.15 m = 15 cm.
  d)   No. Since all the moments would be multiplied by 2, it would stay balanced.
Q2   E.g. The wheelbarrow reduces the amount of force needed to give a particular moment. It does this by having long handles which mean that less force is needed to lift the wheelbarrow, as the point at which the force is applied is further away from the pivot (M = F × d).
Q3   The weight acts at the centre of mass = 40 cm from the pivot. The leg is 80 − 5 = 75 cm from the pivot.
    Anticlockwise moments = Clockwise moments
    40 N × 0.4 m = F × 0.75 m
    16 Nm = F × 0.75 m
    16 ÷ 0.75 = F
    F = 21.3 N

Page 126 — Moments, Stability and Pendulums

Q1   A lot of the mass of the filing cabinet is concentrated in the top draw. So, when the drawer is fully pulled out, the centre of mass could move beyond the edge of the base, making the cabinet unstable.
Q2   C. Because it has the widest base and lowest centre of mass.
Q3 a)   The line of action of the weight lies inside the base of the cart.
  b)   E.g. Having a wider/heavier base to lower the centre of mass.
Q4 a) $f = 1 \div T$, so $T = 1 \div f = 1 \div 1.25 = \textbf{0.8 Hz}$
  b)   Increase the length of the pendulum.

Page 127 — Hydraulics

Q1   flow, incompressible, force, transmitted, pressure, equally
Q2 a)   They use different cross-sectional areas for the effort and load. P = F ÷ A, so a pressure is created at the first piston using a small force over a small area. Pressure is transmitted equally through a liquid, so the pressure at the second piston is the same. The second piston has a larger area — so there will be a much larger force acting on it.
  b) i) $P = F \div A = 650 \div 0.0025 = \textbf{260 000 Pa}$ (or N/m²)
    ii)   The pressure will be the same (260 000 Pa) because pressure is transmitted equally through a liquid — so the pressure at both pistons will be the same.
Q3 a) $P = F \div A = 18 \div 0.00012 = \textbf{150 000 Pa}$ (or N/m²)
  b)   Pressure at smaller piston = pressure at larger piston, so
    $F = P \times A = 150\,000 \times 0.0003 = \textbf{45 N}$

Page 128 — Circular Motion

Q1   D — a change in velocity
Q2 a) and b)

Q3 a)   Yes. It is continually changing direction, so it must be changing velocity — accelerating.
  b)   The following statements should be ticked:
    "If a body is accelerating then there must be a resultant force acting on it."
    "If there is no resultant force acting on a body then it carries on moving in a straight line at the same speed."
  c)   Centripetal force
  d)   A runner running round a circular track — Friction
    A satellite in orbit round the Earth — Gravity
    The seats at the ends of the spokes of a spinning fairground ride — Tension
Q4 a)   greater
  b)   greater
  c)   1617 N

Pages 129-130 — Magnetic Fields

Q1   Magnetic fields can exert a force on a wire carrying a current.
Q2

Physics 3b — Forces and Electromagnetism

Q3 a) It would exert a force of attraction on it.
b) electromagnet
Q4 E.g. Unlike ordinary magnets, electromagnets are magnets which can be switched on and off. So they're useful for attracting and picking up magnetic materials (e.g. iron) so they can be moved, but they can then be made to drop the materials by switching off the current.
Q5 a) When the switch is closed the right-hand contact is attracted towards the solenoid. This breaks the external circuit, turning it off. When the switch is turned off, the solenoid loses its magnetism and the contact is returned to its original position by the spring. This turns the external circuit on again.
b) The soft iron core makes the solenoid more powerful / It has a stronger magnetic force. Soft iron will lose its magnetism quickly when the electric current is switched off.

Page 131 — The Motor Effect

Q1 magnetic field, permanent magnets, force, current, stronger, angle, motor
Q2 a) The wire will move out of the paper (towards the reader).
b) By reversing the direction of the current OR by turning the magnets the other way round (reversing the magnetic field).
Q3 A current-carrying wire will not experience a force if it is parallel to the magnetic field of a permanent magnet.
Q4 The wire will move downwards, at right angles to the magnetic field.

Page 132 — The Simple Electric Motor

Q1 Using a commutator.
Q2 The split-ring commutator reverses the direction of the current every half turn by swapping the contacts to the DC supply.
Q3 By reversing the polarity of the magnets OR by reversing the direction of the current.
Q4 E.g. the axle of the electric motor could be used to turn a (large) pulley wheel, around which the lift cables could wind or unwind to raise or lower the lift.
Q5 current, magnetic, field, force, amplifier, move, frequency, sound.

Page 133 — Electromagnetic Induction

Q1 a) E.g. Electromagnetic induction is the creation of a potential difference across the ends of a conductor which is experiencing a change in magnetic field (as it 'cuts' through magnetic field lines).
b) Move the (vertical) wire in and out of the magnetic field at an angle to the direction of the field (i.e. not parallel to the magnetic field).
c) The ammeter needle would move first in one direction, then back to zero and then in the opposite direction and back to zero again. It would continue like this as long as the wire was moving in and out of the magnetic field.
d) The ammeter needle would still move from one side to the other, but would start from the opposite side.
Q2 a) By pulling the magnet out again OR by turning the magnet round and pushing it into the coil OR by pushing the magnet into the coil from the left-hand side OR by turning the magnet around and pulling it out of the left-hand side of the coil.
b) By pushing the magnet in and immediately pulling it out again.
c) By rapidly pushing the magnet in and out of the coil a number of times.

Q3 E.g. The cog wheel is attached to the bicycle wheel. The cog is attached to a magnet — as the wheel turns, the cog turns and rotates the magnet in a coil of wire on a soft iron core. This induces a potential difference in the coil and a current flows in the wire. The coil is connected in a circuit with the light bulb and so the bulb lights up.

Pages 134-137 — Transformers

Q1 1. A source of alternating potential difference is applied to the primary coil.
2. An alternating current flows in the primary coil.
3. This produces an alternating magnetic field in the iron core.
4. The magnetic field produced inside the secondary coil induces an alternating potential difference at the ends of the secondary coil.
5. If this is applied to an external circuit, an alternating current will flow in that circuit.
Q2 a) When a current flows in the left-hand coil it generates a magnetic field which induces a current in the right hand coil and causes the needle of the ammeter to deflect. Since a current can only be induced when the magnetic field changes, the deflection only occurs when the current is switched on or off.
b) You could put an iron core through the two coils / add more turns to the coils / add more cells to the battery etc. This would make the magnetic field stronger and therefore cause bigger deflections in the ammeter.
Q3 True, false, true.
Q4 A step-down transformer.
Q5 a) A transformer consists of an iron core and two coils.
b) Step-up transformers have more turns on the secondary coil than the primary coil.
c) In a step-down transformer the potential difference across the secondary coil is less than the potential difference across the primary coil.
OR
In a step-up transformer the potential difference across the secondary coil is greater than the potential difference across the primary coil.
Q6 a) The alternating current produces an alternating magnetic field in the core, which in turn induces an alternating potential difference in the secondary coil.
b) Only an alternating current can produce the constantly-changing magnetic field needed to continually induce a voltage in the secondary coil.
Q7 Ash is **wrong** because the iron core carries magnetic field, not current.
Q8 a) True, true, false, true.
b) E.g. any one from: mobile phone chargers / power supplies.
Q9 a) It is a step-down transformer — it reduces the voltage from 240 V to 12 V.
b) i) $P = V \times I = 240 \times 0.25 = \textbf{60 W}$.
ii) $P = V \times I = 12 \times 5 = \textbf{60 W}$.
c) Transformers are nearly 100% efficient.
Q10 The number of turns increases by a factor of 40 so the voltage will also increase by a factor of 40. So the input voltage would need to be $10\,000 \div 40 = \textbf{250 V}$.
Alternatively, use the equation:

$$\frac{V_p}{V_s} = \frac{N_p}{N_s}, \quad \frac{V_p}{10\,000} = \frac{100}{4000}, \quad V_p = \frac{10\,000 \times 100}{4000} = \textbf{250 V}.$$

Physics 3b — Forces and Electromagnetism

Q11

Number of turns on primary coil	Voltage to primary coil (V)	Number of turns on secondary coil	Voltage to secondary coil (V)
1000	12	4000	**48**
1000	**10**	2000	20
1000	12	**1000**	12
71 739	33 000	500	230

Q12 a) Output voltage = 230 V × (8000/5000) = **368 V**.

b) 230 ÷ 20 = 11.5. So there must be 11.5 times more turns on the primary coil than on the secondary. Andy could either:
Keep 5000 turns on the primary coil and adapt the **secondary coil** to have 5000 ÷ 11.5 = **435 turns**.
OR
Keep 8000 turns on the secondary coil and adapt the **primary coil** to have 8000 × 11.5 = **92 000 turns**.

Q13 $V_p \times I_p = V_s \times I_s$
So, $I_p = (V_s \times I_s) \div V_p =$
$(110 \times 20) \div 230 = $ **9.6 A**

Pages 138-140 — Mixed Questions — Physics 3b

Q1 a) Anticlockwise moment = 1000 × 0.6 = 600 Nm
F = 600 ÷ 1.8 = **333 N**

b) The wheelbarrow was tilted so its **centre of mass** moved beyond the edge of its base. This caused a **resultant moment**, causing the wheelbarrow to tip.

c) E.g. the position of the centre of mass, width of the base.

Q2 a) f = 1 ÷ T = 1 ÷ 2 = **0.5 Hz**

b) The force applied to the water at the top of the bag is transmitted to water in other parts of the bag, and causes water to squirt out of the hole.

c) E.g. The large piston has a greater cross-sectional area than the small piston. A small force is applied to the small piston to create a pressure on a liquid. Pressure is transmitted equally through a liquid, so the pressure is the same at the large piston. F = P × A, so there will be a larger force at the larger piston.

Q3 a) The iron core increases the strength of the magnetic field produced by the current in the solenoid.

b) When the switch is closed the electromagnet is turned on, setting up a magnetic field. The iron rocker is attracted towards the electromagnet, so it pivots. This closes the contacts in the motor's circuit and turns the motor on.

Q4 a) The motion tells you which way the forces must be acting — see below.

b) Use Fleming's Left-Hand Rule on one side of the coil. E.g. for the right-hand side of the coil, the field (first finger) goes from right to left (north to south), the motion (thumb) goes upwards, giving you the current (second finger) going into the page.

c) E.g. increase the current, use a stronger magnet.

Q5 a) An alternating potential difference is induced because the coil experiences a magnetic field which is changing (and 'cutting' through the coil).

b) The induced potential difference would be in the opposite direction (when the magnet is at any given position).

Q6 a) gravity

b) i) False

ii) False

c) A

Q7 a) Ratio of turns (secondary:primary) is 200:1000 = 1:5. So the output voltage will be 230 ÷ 5 = **46 V**.

b) i) Iron.

ii) It transfers the magnetic field from the primary to the secondary coil.

c) 33 kV = 33 000 V. Then:
Secondary voltage/Primary voltage = 230/33 000. So No. of turns on secondary coil = 2000 × 230 ÷ 33 000 = 14 turns.

d) E.g. they are lighter and smaller than traditional transformers and so are useful for lightweight devices like chargers. They are also more efficient, as they don't use much power when plugged in but have no load (i.e. a mobile phone) attached.